Analysis of Data Integrity Schemes in Cloud

Hariharasitaraman S

Analysis of Data Integrity Schemes in Cloud

First Edition December 2023

Written by Hariharasitaraman S

TABLE OF CONTENTS

LIST OF TABLES

LIST OF FIGURES

LIST OF ABBREVIATIONS AND SYMBOLS

AES	-	Advanced Encryption Standards
AGCD	-	Approximate Greatest Common Divisor
API	-	Application Programming Interfaces
APR	-	Apache Portable Runtime
AWS	-	Amazon Web Services
BGV	-	Brakerski-Gentry-Vaikuntanathan's
BLS	-	Boneh–Lynn–Shacham
CloudSim	-	Cloud Simulator
CPABE	-	Ciphertext-Policy Attribute-Based Encryption
CPDP	-	Cooperative Provable Data Possession
CSP	-	Cloud Service Providers
CSV	-	Comma Separated Value
DaaS	-	Database as a Service
DGHV	-	Dijk, Gentry, Halevi and Vaikuntanathan's
DIaaS	-	Data Integrity as a Service
DPDP	-	Dynamic Provable Dynamic Possession
EUCALYPTUS	-	Elastic Utility Computing Architecture for Linking Your Programs to Useful Systems
FADE	-	File Assured DEletion Protocol
FECC	-	Forward Error-Correcting Code
FHE	-	Fully Homomorphic Encryption
FHEISK	-	FHE scheme using Integers with Smaller Key length
FMT	-	Fractal Merkle Tree
GCE	-	Google Compute Engine
GSuite	-	Google Suite
HAIL	-	High-Availability and Integrity Layer

HE	-	Homomorphic Encryption
HIS	-	Health Information Systems
IaaS	-	Infrastructure as a Service
IMAP	-	Internet Message Access Protocol
IoT	-	Internet of Things
IPECC	-	Integrity-Protected Error-Correcting Code
KB	-	Kilo Byte
KGC	-	Key Generation Centre
log	-	Logarithmic
LwE	-	Learning with Errors
MAC	-	Message Authentication Code
MB	-	Mega Byte
MHT	-	Merkle Hash Tree
MP	-	Multi-Party
MRPDPS	-	Multiple Replicas Provable Data Possession Scheme
ms	-	milli seconds
MT	-	Merkle Tree
NIST	-	National Institute of Standards and Technology
PaaS	-	Platform as a Service
PDP	-	Provable Data Possession
PKI	-	Public Key Infrastructure
PMT	-	Position aware Merkle Tree
PoR	-	Proof of Retrievability
PoS	-	Proof of Storage
PRNG	-	Pseudo–Random Number Generator
Proxy PDP	-	Proxy Provable data Possession
QoS	-	Quality of Service
RSA	-	Rivest Shamir Adleman

SaaS	-	Software as a Service
SAP	-	Systems Applications and Products
SCO	-	Self-Controlling Objects
SEAL	-	Simple Encrypted Arithmetic Library
SHA	-	Secure Hash Algorithm
SHE	-	Somewhat Homomorphic Encryption
SHIELD	-	Scalable Homomorphic Implementation of Encrypted Data
SLA	-	Service Level Agreement
TPA	-	Third-Party Auditors
TPG	-	Third-Party aGent
TTP	-	Trusted Third Party
USD	-	United States Dollar
UUID	-	Universally Unique IDentifier
VDM	-	Verifiable Data Model
VFHE	-	Verifiable Fully Homomorphic Encryption
VM	-	Virtual Machines
YYYY-MM-DD	-	Year-Month-Date

SYMBOLS

λ	-	Security Parameter
γ	-	Bit-Length of eachInput
η	-	Bit-Length of Secret Key
ρ	-	Bit-Length of The Noise
τ	-	Number of Elements in the Public Key
ρ'	-	Secondary Noise Parameter for Encryption
S_k	-	Secret Key or Private Key
P_k	-	Public Key
c	-	Cipher Text
L	-	Skip List
H	-	Hash Function
p	-	Prime Numbers
r,q	-	Random Integers
b	-	Data Blocks
C	-	Evaluation Circuit

CHAPTER 1

INTRODUCTION

1.1 INTRODUCTION TO CLOUD LANDSCAPE

The National Institute of Standards and Technology (NIST) defines cloud computing as a web-based paradigm that facilitates the deployment of flexible and cost-effective business models, throughthe sharing of expensive resources for computation such as storage, applications, infrastructure, networks, services, data, etc. It is the most sought-after platform for hosting various solutions by service providers due to its scalability to radical changes in the client population. Clients recognize the potential of cloud computing platforms and rely on Cloud Service Providers (CSP) to harness the versatility of this environment in exploiting business solutions, outsourcing sensitive data and computations. Cloud computing has witnessed a phenomenal growth in diverse aspects such as physical infrastructure, deployment models, protocol architectures, security mechanisms, etc., providing reliable solutions in various domains.

The fundamentals of cloud computing are very well-documented in the pioneering works of Fox et al. [1] and Knorrand Gruman [2]. Cloud computing is viewed as an integrated platform for data storage, deployment of business models, delivery of services, sharing resources, etc., and enabling resource-constrained clients to access various services at low cost. All the cloud computing models must be designed with the following characteristics to provide efficientservices.

- On-demand self-service: Clients can access storage and computing resources directly from service providers.

- Broad network access: Clients can utilize computing facilities distributed across networks using heterogeneous resource-constrained devices.
- Resource pooling: Multiple clients can dynamically access physical and virtual resources on-demand from a pool of resources organized with a multi-tenancy model.
- Location independence: Clients can dynamically access resources hosted by multiple providers irrespective of physical locations.
- Elasticity: Clients can rapidly access and release the required resources at any instant.
- Measured service: Clients and providers of major services are well-informedof the utilization of resources through monitoring and reporting mechanisms.

Cloud computing services are generally offered in three models, namely, Software as a Service (SaaS), Platform as a Service (PaaS), and Infrastructure as a Service (IaaS).

- **Software as a Service (SaaS)**

Software as aService is also referred to as a cloud application service. In this model, third-party hosts a software application in the cloud for access to clients. The service can be run in a client browser without any software download or installation. Issues with data, network, and devices are managed by the service providers, enabling the clients to run their business without any interruption. Google GSuite, Salesforce, Dropbox, CiscoWebEx, SAP Concur, and GoToMeeting are some of the widely used SaaS.

- **Platform as a Service (PaaS)**

PaaS model, otherwise called cloud platform service, provides a framework enabling the clients to build customized applications. This framework is delivered as a development platform for the client over the web. It provides complete freedom to the developers in building the software, relieving the clients from issues connected with storage, infrastructure, operating system, and software. Windows Azure, Google App Engine, OpenShift, Amazon Web Service (AWS) Elastic Beanstalk, Heroku and Force.comare some of the PaaS's used in business applications for streamlining workflows among multiple developers.

- **Infrastructure as a Service (IaaS)**

Cloud infrastructure services called IaaS comprise highly scalable and automated computing resources. These service models employ virtualization technology for the delivery of servers, networks, operating systems, and storage to clients. These resources are dynamically used by clients as services on demand.

Clients employ IaaS such as Digital Ocean, Google Compute Engine (GCE), Linode, Rackspace, Cisco Metacloud and Microsoft Azure for evolving infrastructure requirements during the course of theimplementation. These service models are offered to clients through cloud deployment models categorized as public, private and hybrid clouds based on their location, as depicted in Figure 1.1.

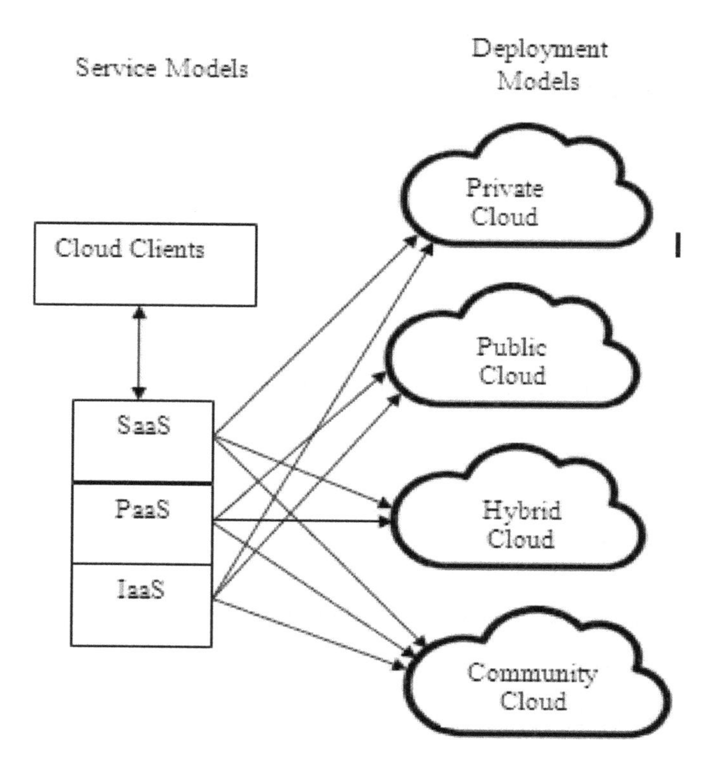

Figure 1.1 Cloud Infrastructure

- **Private Cloud**

This kind of cloud is established exclusively for an organization, maintained in its internal data centre or hosted by a third party. The services and infrastructure accessible through a private network are dedicated entirely to the organization, enabling it to devise customized solutions to meet business needs. These clouds are used by organizations running controlled applications in a confined environment, exercising complete control of data and resources.

- **Public Cloud**

In a public deployment model, cloud service providers own and operate resources such as servers and storage, allowing the clients to access them over the internet on a pay-per-usage basis. The clients use public clouds for web applications such as mailing and office solutions, data outsourcing, application development, and hosting.

- **Hybrid Cloud**

This model which is an integration of the private and the public clouds of an organization offers a high degree of security, flexibility, and scalability to accommodate dynamic business workflows. In this model, the private cloud is used for the storage of confidential data and running critical enterprise applications. The public cloud hosts services such as external data storage, web applications for mailing, file transfer services, etc. This model supports the transition of data and services between private and public clouds according to business needs. A hybrid cloud can be hosted both internally and externally.

- **Community Cloud**

This is a kind of private cloud exclusive to a community of enterprises. Itfunctions like similar business models. These communities collaborate over the cloud to deploy projects, applications, and business solutions. Hence, they have similar resource requirements from the cloud environment for the accomplishment of business objectives. Common management policies are enforced to enable addressing security and performance constraints which are identical for all the community members.This kind of cloud is hosted internally or by a third-party service provider.

It is seen from Figure 1.1 that the cloud computing environment is an integrated environment of service models, deployment models, resources, services, data, network client and server. Cloud-based services are customer-centric and designed in tune withthe client requirements. Storage is one of the major requirements of enterprises to host applications and store data. Cloud storage service is a new standard of cloud services concerned with the allocation of shared storage among multiple clients simultaneously.

Cloud storage providers maintain data in protected physical storage devices distributed across multiple locations. They ensure the availability and accessibility of data to clients through well-designed virtual machine images and web service interfaces. Cloud storage providers are confronted with performance and security concerns and spend huge amounts to meet these requirements.

One of the major security requirements is the reliability of client data residing at remote storage devices, on outsourcing to the server. Evolution in cloud computing has led to the development of new service categories such as Storage as a Service [3], Security as a Service [4], Data Integrity as a Service (DIaaS) [5], etc. In cloud storage models, the client does not have control over data, once the data is outsourced to remote servers. Though Service Level Agreements (SLA) exist between the client and service providers, the clients do not entirely trust them.

Usually, Third-Party Auditors (TPAs) are employed by service providers to establish trust. The multi-tenancy feature of the cloud allows the sharing of data among multiple users functioning at different locations. Security vulnerabilities [6] and synchronization errors may result in loss of, damage to and lack of updation of data. Hence, DIaaS has gained immense attention among researches and new schemes for data integrity verification have been proposed. In the following subsections, the need for robust approaches for data integrity verification, design issues and the generic architecture of integrity verification mechanisms is discussed.

1.2 CLOUD STORAGE CONCERNS AND DATA INTEGRITY SCHEMEREQUIREMENTS

In recent years, many schemes for data integrity verification have been implemented. The earliest scheme in this context is the blockless verification approach proposed byChen et al. [7]. It makes a considerable reduction in communication overhead and computational cost involved in retrieving the entire outsourced client data for verification. This scheme is based on metadata created from the client data before outsourcing. The owner of the data generates a verifiable proof from the metadata for ensuring data integrity and also verifies it with the metadata, instead of the entire client data.

Initially, data integrity schemes were developed for fixed or add-on data as in [8] and later extended to dynamic modifications, insertions, and deletions on client data. Further, under these schemes' verification could be done by only one entity, which could be the data owner or a trusted auditor. The concept of verification by multiple entities, either including or excluding TPAs was introduced by Wang et al. [9]. However, verification by TPAs raised data leakage and privacy issues which were averted by privacy-preserving verification schemes proposed by Erway et al. [10].

Further, for reliability and accessibility requirements, multiple copies of data are distributed across storage devices. The early schemes on integrity verification for a single copy of data were extended to multiple copies in [11]. Also, new schemes addressing various data storage issues such as data geolocation [12], integration of multiple clouds [13], data deduplication [14] and proof of data retrievability [15] were introduced.

Blockless integrity check mechanisms employ different mathematical approaches for the creation of metadata for reducing security risks and overheads. These approaches include Cauchy matrix-based RS codes in [16], fountain codes of Shi et al. [17], algebraic signatures by Yu et al. [18] and homomorphic authentication tags proposed by Wang and Zhang [19].

However, there are differences among verification schemes in matters relating to overheads in computation, exchange of data between entities, data access, and retrieval from storage that have an influence on theefficiency of these approaches.

Cloud data storage and retrieval mechanisms employed in a cloud environment, make a significant contribution to the efficiency of the integrity check mechanisms. Recently, the clients are after an important feature called the unbounded queries, enabling data verification without any restrictions on the frequency and time interval of verifications. This kind of extreme requirement can be granted to the clients only with the deployment of best data archival and retrieval techniques in cloud storage devices. Frequent access and verification of data also demand integrity verification algorithms with low computational and storage overheads.

The efficacy of cloud-based computation mainly relies on cloud storage management, access control, and integrity verification mechanisms. There exist numerous challenges in the design of integrity verification mechanisms which are the results of trade-offs between performance and Quality of Service (QoS).

1.3 DESIGN CONSIDERATIONS OF DATA INTEGRITY SCHEMES

Various access control, security and privacy issues with cloud storage are detailed in the works of Chow et al. [20], Zissis and Lekkas [21] and Rao and Selvamani [22]. Particularly, Avram [23] presents the merits and challenges of adopting cloud computing in enterprise solutions, analyzing various factors. The major concerns in the deployment of integrity check mechanisms in the cloud environment are dealt with this section and the design parameters central to the integrity check mechanisms are identified.

1.3.1 Entity identification and management

Confidentiality and integrity requirements of outsourced data in the cloud environment are realized in the cloud environment by impeccable management of entities and access control mechanisms. As the data owner is relieved from control over outsourced data, tracking the data access by the owner and other stakeholders is important. Different entities in the cloud employ authentication mechanisms central to their organization. A unified authentication and authorization mechanism is essential exclusively for accessing cloud data to ensure the protection of the data from unauthorized access.The focus must be on categorizing the entities, with their unique identification and prioritization with access privileges. The File Assured Deletion (FADE) protocol proposed by Tang et al. [24] supports key management,data integrity and privacy in the cloud.

1.3.2 Data format

Regulations for internal data representation and management in the cloud have not been defined so far. The service providers follow their own internal standards found suitable for storage devices.Clients associated with a service provider experience interoperability and data migration issues on mobility from one server to another in multi-cloud environments. The definition of universal standards for data formats can facilitate data access and integrity verification.

1.3.3 Malicious internal attacks

Threats are posed on cloud data internally by employees, business partners and third-party business collaborators of an organization, resulting in loss of confidentiality and integrity of data. Organizations find it difficult to cope with these attacks due to diverse attack patterns and difficulty in distinguishing the attacker from genuine entitiesand the origin of attacks. An attack of this kind can be prevented through enforcement of strict access control mechanisms, reducing the number of privileges to users and continuous logging of data access and manipulation activities. A detailed account of the internal attacks on cloud data is indicated in the works of Duncan et al. [25] and Khorshed et al. [26].

1.3.4 Malicious external attacks

Attacks launched on network, data, and infrastructure from the external environment by outsiders called external attacks, are highly precarious in cloud environments. The severity of such attacks is catastrophic, causing financial loss, affecting the reputation of an organization and causing loss of trust for clients. It is very difficult to trace the origins of such attacks. In a virtual distributed environment, the data require frequent reorganization and encryption of sensitive data. The difficulty in launching attacks and deciphering data render these attacks useless to an adversary. Hybrid intrusion detection systems considering various potential points for attack, proposed in the work of Hatef et al. [27] can mitigate these attacks.

1.3.5 Availability

The ability of the CSP to provide the services demanded by the client anytime, called availability, is one of the most essential requirements of cloud computing. This service must be assured of various resources such as data, computing, and infrastructure. The service provider should incorporate high-end hardware, ubiquitous computing provisions, efficient information retrieval, and flawless security mechanisms, in the cloud environment for assurance of a high degree of availability. Consequently, high availability requirements call for meeting unique security challenges in a distributed environment, with physical and virtual resources accessible to multiple clients. A detailed review of the reliability and availability requirements in the cloud environment is presented by Mesbahi et al. [28].

1.3.6 Trusted Third Party (TTP)

Employment of aTTP has been a common practice for over two decades as in [29] for the establishment of trust between the clients and service providers to assure data confidentiality, integrity, and authenticity. The TTP facilitates secure end-to-end transactions between two parties in various domains. Trust is established between two interacting entities based on security parameters, conventions, and techniques agreed-upon through TTP. These entities are connected to the TTP through well-designed trust chains and Public Key Infrastructure (PKI). However, clients are concerned over allowing the TTP the facility of access to their sensitive data fearing data tampering. Hence, the security protocols should employ symmetric cryptographic techniques for ensuring data integrity and protection to data and asymmetric techniques for the implementation of PKI. Homomorphic encryption schemes which create an abstraction between the data and operations are ideal for cloud computing environments with Third Party Auditor (TPA)s.

1.3.7 Dynamism in business models

Though enterprises design their business models suitable for access over the cloud, they introduce customization frequently to enrich client interactivity. However, this may lead to a breach of security and introduce new vulnerabilities. The baselines of business models should ensure being intact after customization. The impact of the transformation of a conventional business model to a cloud-based model is presented by Nieuwenhuis et al.[30]. This paper highlights the need for data integrity mechanisms to ensure data has not tamperedwith a multi-client business environment.

1.3.8 Service Level Agreement (SLA)

Transforming traditional business solutions to cloud-based solutions is challenging for organizations due to the risks involved in delivering quality services relying on cloud service providers. SLAs define the operating parameters between the clients and service providers with the assurance of satisfaction with the quality requirements. Researchers have identified trivial and non-trivial parameters for inclusion in the SLA [31] including usability, service guarantee, error rate, accountability, and privacy, etc. Accountability and privacy are generally combined into a single non-trivial factor, emphasizing the support for tracking the activities of individual entities and controlled access to data.

1.3.9 Data forensics

Investigation of security attacks in the cloud environment is challenging due to its distributed nature. The collection of digital evidence on data security breach is difficult due to the multi-tenancy feature. Further, the evidence [32] gathered differs with respect to the service and deployment models. Data tampering is highly pronounced in hybrid models in which there is a frequent transition from public to private clouds. Optimized high-speed data integrity verification mechanisms are essential for verifying the integrity of data rapidly, after dynamic updates by the clients.

1.3.10 Data sharing

Data sharing is a widely used cloud service due to its flexibility and cost-effectiveness. Heavy computational overheads and weak data security are the characteristics of existing data sharing solutions. Li et al. [33] have proposed an attribute-based, fine-grained approach for selective data sharing for resource-constrained devices. Similarly, the designing of integrity check mechanisms requires, addressing the size of data shared among the entities.

1.4 THE ARCHITECTURE OF DATA INTEGRITY SCHEMES

Data integrity verification schemes are generally implemented with three entities,namely, the client, service provider, and the TPA. The schematic of the generic integrity verification scheme is given in Figure 1.2. This process is based on the challenge-response authentication protocol. This protocol is analogous to the question-answer model in which the challenge refers to a question and the response refers to the answer. This model is basically employed in password authentication where the verifier asks for the password and the client responds with a password.

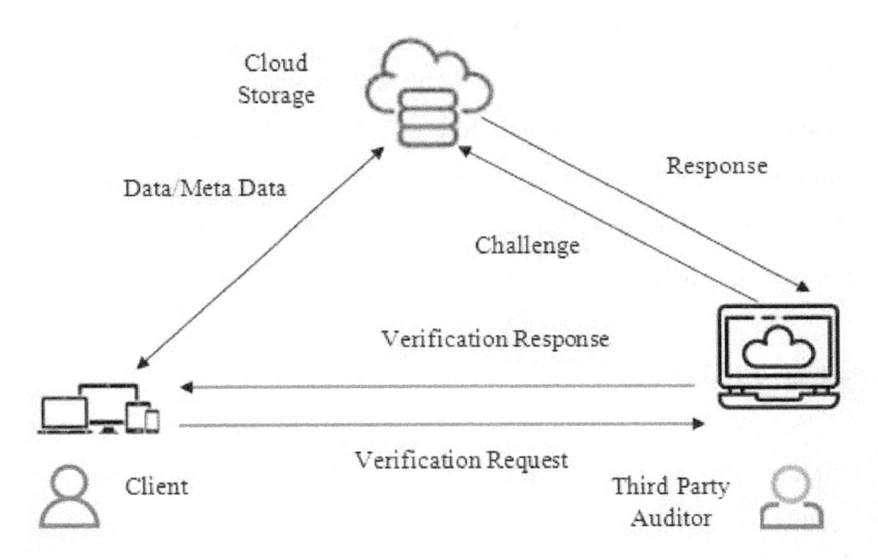

Figure 1.2 Data Integrity Verification

This model is extended to the data verification mechanism which consists of two phases, namely, challenge creation and verification. Initially, the confidential data owned by the client is outsourced to the service provider which stores the data in remote storage devices. For integrity verification, the client places the request to the TPA. The challenge is computed by the TPA based on metadata and is sent to the server. The response to this challenge is computed by the server and forwarded to the TPA, whichverifies the proof for integrity and forwards the same to the client.With the generic scheme depicted in Figure 1.2 as the foundation, many variants of data integrity check mechanisms have been introduced and categorized with respect to the implementation parameters, these are discussed in Chapter 2.

1.5 PROBLEM STATEMENT

Data integrity solutions are integral to cloud environments for establishing trust among the entities and assurance of the reliability of solutions. Implementation of integrity verification mechanisms is challenging in multi-cloud environments due to the high degree of diversities in business models and client requirements. Similarly, concerns about security, design, resource utilization, and system functionalities are very severe in heterogeneous environments. In this research, the significance of these issues are seen and novel PDP models have been proposed for integrity verification for the sensitive rehabilitation services in a multi-cloud healthcare environment.

1.5.1 Research questions

The research questions addressed and the methodologies for finding solutions are discussed in this subsection.

Research question 1: How are healthcare services offered with cloud computing at present?

Extensive literature review with cloud computing based healthcare services shows that these services are centred on the enterprise models of the healthcare organizations, completely relying on the services providers.

Research question 2: What are the contributing factors associated with the acceptanceof health clouds by the clients?

Low cost On-demand data storage and retrieval services protecting the privacy and security of client data are the requirements of the cloud-based healthcare service models for acceptance by clients. Capability of the service providers to establish trust and security mechanisms is key to retain the clients.

Research question 3: What are the security requirements of cloud-based healthcare service models?

Several security issues manifest in medical clouds due to multi-provider cloud solutions incorporating several collaborators. The trade-off between on-demand dynamic healthcare cloud services and privacy concerns of the subjects exerts great demands on the security mechanisms deployed at the data servers by the service providers. These mechanisms include authentication, confidentiality, integrity verification and authorization.

Research question 4: How do the security requirements differ in cloud based rehabilitation services?

The security requirements for rehabilitation services are the same as conventional hospital based healthcare services. Most of the rehabilitation services are delivered at resource-constrained environments such as homes, small remote healthcare institutions etc. which are susceptible to unauthorized access. Design of security mechanisms for rehabilitation services are highly challenging to the vulnerabilities in these uncontrolled environments.

Research Question 5: What are the perceived security requirements of the healthcare models for rehabilitation services?

The following are the security requirements identified for rehabilitation services, as evident from the literature review.

i. Dynamic models for establishing trust by proof of verification.
ii. Space efficient dynamic service models facilitating trace of the path of data retrieval to resolve trust-based issues.
iii. Exclusive data integrity verification mechanisms for rehabilitation services.
iv. Encryption algorithms enabling manipulation of encoded data.

1.5.2 Hypothesis

This research is based on the following hypotheses.

Hypothesis 1. Security and Privacy concerns on patients' information influence the acceptability of the healthcare cloud services.

Establishing privacy preserving mechanisms in accessing patient data has a significant impact on the clients and reinforces their trust on the reliability of the service providers. This considerably reduces the concerns on the individuals regarding the security of their data.

Hypothesis 2. Dynamic models for establishing trust by verification of proofs can enhance the trust of clients on the reliability of the system.

It is essential for cloud service providers to establish beyond doubt that the client data is accessible and can be manipulated by authorized clients only. This can be proved by mathematical computations involving secure client-side data.

Hypothesis 3. Verification models capable of tracing information access can be used to resolve security issues in distributed healthcare cloud environments.

Cloud computing environments are characterized by heavy client dynamics due to the rapid movement of the clients between multiple clouds. It is possible that data is uploaded, modified and deleted by authorized by clients in a short span of time. These operations are performed in multiple storage devices distributed across cloud networks. It is essential to keep track of the origin of requests for various operations and prove the data retrieval path encompassing the storage devices unambiguously to win the trust of the clients.

Hypothesis 4. Authentication and data integrity verification schemes can enhance the quality of rehabilitation services in the cloud environment.

Generally, a subset of patient information stored in the cloud is frequently accessed by the care providers. It is vital to ensure that the most recent updates are available for the caregivers to devise the treatment plans. In rehabilitation services, authentication and integrity verifications are essential to prevent abuse of patient data and fasten the delivery of care

Hypothesis 5. Algorithms for manipulation of encrypted data can protect the data from unauthorized access and accidental or intentional manipulations

Instead of manipulating the client data directly, manipulation of encrypted client data can protect the data from unauthorized access. Homomorphic encryption (HE) schemes facilitate computations on encrypted data without affecting the underlying original data. Authentication and integrity verification mechanisms for rehabilitation services can be implemented with HE schemes to protect the privacy and security of patient data.

1.6 THESIS OBJECTIVES

This research is aimed at building robust PDPs focusing on client dynamics suitable for the highly secured healthcare multi-cloud environment, with special attention on remote rehabilitation services. Provision of these services in a heterogeneous cloud environment, complying with medical standards requires flexible, swift, fault-free and reliable integrity verification mechanisms.In addition to the above intrinsic features, the ability to perform integrity checks by service providers and Third-Party Auditors (TPA) without revealing the original client data is the much-sought requirement of data owners. Considering the above requirements, the research objectives are defined as follows.

- To design and analyzea dynamic PDP model for multi-cloud using skip list and Merkle Hash Tree (MHT).
- To design and analyzea computational and space-efficient, dynamic PDP model with authentication path verification using Fractal Merkle Tree (FMT).
- To design and analyzea dynamicintegrity verification scheme for client data in a multi-cloud environment for health rehabilitation services employing Position aware Merkle Tree (PMT).
- To design and analyzea fully homomorphic encryption-baseddata integrity assurance scheme for dynamic client operations inthe cloud.

It is seen that the objectives of this research are aligned on the research questions and hypothesis presented in the previous subsections. It is evident that implementation of the proposed system with the above objectives can improve the quality of rehabilitation services assuring security and privacy of patient data.

1.7 RESEARCH METHODOLOGIES

The methodologies followed in this research are purely empirical followed by statistical analyses. The proposed systems are implemented and tested with the Matlab 2017b software. In line with the objectives listed in Section 1.5 each of the objectives is realized with the implementation of a security mechanism. The schematics of these subsystems are presented in respective subsection with algorithms. The performance of the proposed systems are evaluated with bench mark data for insertion, deletion and updation operations with the Statistical Analysis Tool Box of Matlab 2017b.

By exercising the security mechanisms with well-designed test cases, the accomplishment of the objectives of this research are verified.

1.8 ORGANIZATION OF THE THESIS

Chapter 1 presents an elaborateanalysis ofthe cloud landscape, issues in cloud-based storage, need, design and architecture of data integrity schemes and the classifications of data integrity verification schemes. Chapter 2 presents a detailed review of the literature pertaining to data security mechanisms spanning the earliest to the most recent works in this context, for identification of the research gaps and defining the research objectives.

Chapters 3,4 and5,elaborates three novel PDPs exploiting the capabilities of MHTs, skip lists, FMT, and PMTs for dynamic client operations related to rehabilitation services in a multi-cloud environment. Chapter 6 presents a novel Homomorphic Encryption (HE) based integrity verification mechanism, protecting the client data from direct manipulations. Chapter 7 provides the conclusions arrived at and directions for further investigations.

The contents of the chapters are detailed below.

Chapter 1 This section contains an introduction to cloud infrastructure, storage issues in the cloud, need for data integrity verification mechanisms, design challenges, the architecture of integrity verification schemes, the nomenclature of data integrity verification, etc.Further, the research objectives and outlook of the thesis are also given in this section.

Chapter 2 This section presents the literature survey with a thorough review of the fundamental and recent research in the construction of PDPs and advocates the need for the proposed system.

Chapter 3 In this chapter, the architecture and algorithms of the proposed Dynamic PDP based on both MHT and skip listsare explained in detail. The efficacy of the model is demonstrated with extensive experiments, quantitative metrics and performance analyses.

Chapter 4 This chapter demonstrates a dynamic PDP model based on FMT for a multi-cloud environment, harnessing the representation of minimal trees. This model is evaluated with suitable test cases and a detailed analysis of performance characteristics is given.

Chapter 5 This chapter describes the implementation of the PMT based system togetherwith evaluation metrics for client data operations, space, computational, and time complexities in a medical multi-cloud environment.

Chapter 6 This chapter presents a homomorphic encryption scheme suitable for the public integrity verification mechanism, completely protecting the client data from intentional and accidental modifications. An integrity verification system designed with this scheme exhibits minimum communication and computational overheads with electronic patient records in a multi-cloud environment.

Chapter 7 This section presents a summary of the research findings and prospective avenues for further investigations.

1.8 SUMMARY

The large-scale use of cloud computing is seen in all kinds of service domains, irrespective of the size of the enterprises. There has also been a significant increase in the threats to client data with this growth. Data integrity is identified as very basic, yet a major requirement, in cloud computing environments. Rather than an assurance of the integrity of client data, it refers to the assurance of a broad range of complex aspects such as geographical locations, hardware, algorithms, data objects, deletion and duplication operations, etc. Threats to data integrity are numerous and their severity can break the trust of the clients, reliability of the solutions and reputation of the business.

Hence, data integrity verification has been the subject of extensive research in various dimensions such as deployment models, verification algorithms, evaluation procedures, data migration, etc. Above all, data integrity verification algorithms constitute a significant domain for research with wide scope for investigations in various facets such as proof generation, key generation, verification, data structures, integrity aspects, client dynamics, solutions for resource-constrained devices, etc.

CHAPTER 2

LITERATURE SURVEY

2.1 INTRODUCTION

This section presents a review of various research works relevant to this research work and its objectives. Extensive studies have been carried out by analysis of literature, focusing on various implementation methodologies, deployment platforms, performance measures, and applications.The emphasis of this review is on establishing the proof of the concepts underlying the proposed models, from the fundamental and most recent investigations. The outcomes of this review are basic to the identification of mathematical concepts and methodologies to be employed in this research.

The results of this literature review are organized into four subsections for a comprehensive depiction of the existing research works and identification of their limitations. Initially, a broad taxonomy of the integrity verification schemes based on the implementation strategies is given. This is followed by an analysis of the data structures suitable for the design of the proposed systems and their applications in the existing PDPs. Finally, the homomorphic encryption schemes and the cryptographic systems in which they are deployed are analyzed.

2.2 DATA INTEGRITY VERIFICATION SCHEME CLASSES

This section presents a complete taxonomy of the data integrity verification mechanisms classified on the basis of attributes such as domain, client data type, nature of metadata, application, and cryptographic algorithm employed and the mode of verification, as below. Figure 2.1. is the diagrammatic representation of the taxonomy.

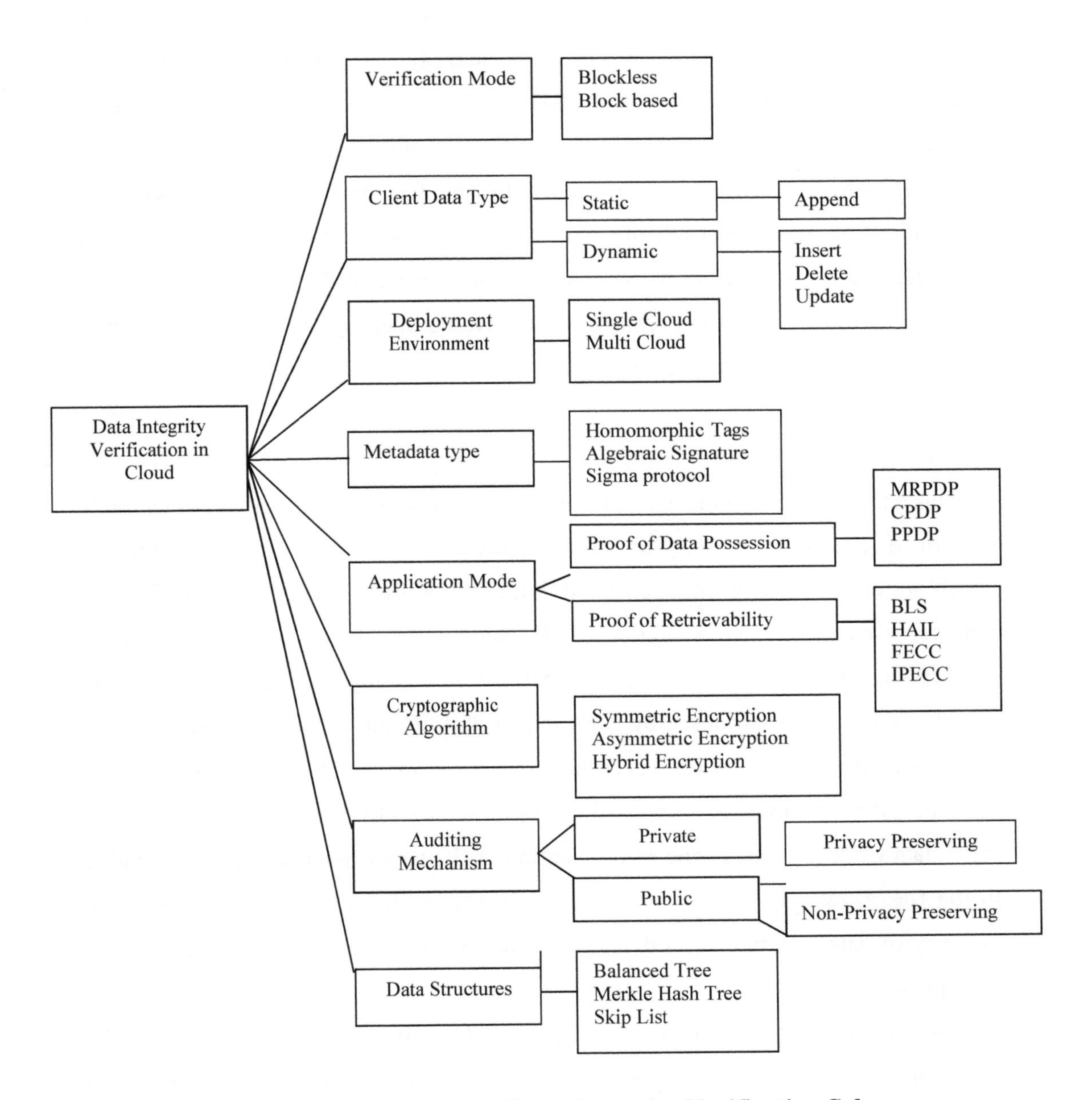

Figure 2.1 Taxonomy of Data Integrity Verification Schemes

2.2.1 Mode of verification

There are two modes of verification, namely, block-based and blockless verification schemes, based on the manner in which the integrity verificationis performed. The blockless schemes of Deswarte et al. [34] and Han et al. [35], called deterministic schemes access the entire data file for the verification of integrity and provided a 100% guarantee. These schemes are constrained by the file sizes and the frequency of verifications arising as a result of the computational and communication overheads involved. The block-based or probabilistic schemes introduced by Ateniese et al. [36, 37] simplified the verification process by performing integrity checks on only a small block of data sampled from the entire file.

2.2.2 Client data type

This attribute refers to the nature of the client data on which integrity verification is performed. The client data may be static like file archival, libraries, data backup, etc., which are either static or only appended, but not modified. The integrity verification scheme proposed by Yuan and Yu [38] operates on static data. Data integrity verification schemes on dynamic data generated by creating, read, update and delete operations have been proposed by Curtmola et al. [39] and Zhang and Blanton [40]. These schemes employ specialized data structures for rapid verification of data. Similarly, the first approach proposed by Ateniese et al. [37] verifies the integrity of static data while it demands the recomputation of file tags when new data is appended to the file. However, the scheme proposed in [8] by the same authors verifies the integrity of data resulting from dynamic client operations such as updation, deletion and append.

The data integrity verification scheme proposed by Erway et al.[10] does not restrict the number of queries but supports dynamic insertion, deletion, modification, and updating operations. Dynamic operations on client data are accomplished through the employment of efficient data structures such as the Flex list and skip list by Esiner et al., [41].

The scheme proposed by Dodis et al. [42], is a versatile scheme based on the complexity theory which provides optimal POR solutions considering variants such as bounded-use, unbounded-use, knowledge-soundness, information-soundness, etc. Further, tolerance to errors is a vital requirement of integrity verification schemes. Such a scheme introduced by Bowers et al. [43], is based on incremental encoding performs integrity verification with voluminous data sets. The scheme proposed by Barsoum and Hasan [44], performs integrity verification on multiple copies of data, with verification time independent of the number of copies of client data.

2.2.3 Deployment environment

This attribute denotes the cloud environment in which the scheme for integrity verification is implemented. A detailed review of deployment models and service models shows wide variations in the requirements of data integrity verification schemes with the underlying cloud architecture of an organization. The functionality of hybrid clouds requires a highly flexible and robust data integrity verification scheme compared to others. A collaborative scheme for assuring data possession based on hash indexing and homomorphically verifiable responses exclusively for hybrid clouds has been proposed by Zhu et al., [45].

However, an earlier scheme proposed by Curtmola et al. [39] which generates multiple copies of client data and handles data operations with multiple storage servers is restricted to a single cloud. Later, Zhu et al. [13] extended their homomorphic scheme to a multi-cloud environment with additional security provisions based on multi-prover zero-knowledge proof verification.

2.2.4 Metadata type

Data integrity schemes are based on computations on metadata to reduce communication and computational overheads and prevent data loss and abuse. Homomorphic tags created by the Rivest-Shamir-Adleman (RSA) algorithm, which are encrypted forms of client data have been used as metadata in [37]. The sigma protocol-based system proposed by Mohan and Katti [46], transmits a small amount of data from the client to the server in the challenge-response process and maintains minimal data at the client for proof verification. This scheme operating on small client data reduces the overheads and client-side computations. Later, other schemes based on homomorphic tags have been proposed by Yuan and Yu[38], Zhang and Blanton[40] and Zhu et al. [13]. Metadata derived from algebraic signatures were also used in the schemes of Luo and Bai [52] and Tate et al. [47].

2.2.5 Application mode

This attribute determines the mode of application of the integrity verification process. Though integrity verification refers to verification of the intact characteristics of data, it is generally employed in two contexts, namely,the Provable Data Possession (PDP) and Proof of Retrievability (POR). The PDP schemes which are probabilistic in nature, which performs the verification process with block samples of the client data file. These schemes are homomorphic in nature with computations on metadata. While these schemes identify tampering in data, they do not support the recovery of corrupted data. Variants of PDP systems proposed include the Multiple Replicas Provable Data Possession Scheme (MR-PDP) [39], and Cooperative PDP (CPDP) [13, 19]. In the Proxy PDP (PPDP) proposed by Wang [48], the concept of employing a client proxy for verification of the integrity was introduced to free the client from computational burdens.

PDP schemes can be transformed into POR schemes through the infusion of error correction codes. These schemes are implemented with all client data residing at the CSP,to enable retrievability of the data by the client. Two POR schemes for static data based on Boneh–Lynn–Shacham (BLS) signatures and pseudorandom functions are proposed by Shacham and Waters [49]. These schemes feature long queries, short responses, private verification, deterministic verification, unbounded queries, etc. However, data leakage is a major limitation of these schemes. The POR scheme introduced by Erway et al.[10] employs rank-based authenticated skip list data structure to support rapid operations on client data and unbounded queries.

The High-Availability and Integrity Layer (HAIL) scheme proposed by Bowers et al. [43] employs the Integrity-Protected Error-Correcting Code (IP-ECC) for data recovery.Similarly,Chen et al. [7] employed network codes for data backup and archival in a distributed storage environment. Ateniese et al. [50] extended the PDP scheme proposed earlier to a POR scheme, employing Forward Error-Correcting Codes (FEC).

2.2.6 Cryptographic algorithm

The cryptographic scheme employed in the implementation of PDP or POR systems is a very significant attribute for the classification of integrity verification schemes. Symmetric, asymmetric cryptographic schemes and their combinations used in integrity verification are based on the security requirements. The scheme proposed by Ateniese et al. [37], involves the creation ofprivate with symmetric keys of the asymmetric RSA algorithm by homomorphic tags and the use of cryptographic hash functions in the creation of metadata. Similarly, the schemes, seen in their works proposed byCurtmola et al. [39], Wang [51] and Zhu et al.[13] are also based on symmetric cryptography. Integrity verification systems employ symmetric cryptographic algorithms for confidentiality requirements.

Asymmetric cryptographic systems are used in the implementation of the security mechanism with both confidentiality and authentication requirements. The schemes proposed by Barsoum and Hasan [44], Luo and Bai [52], Shen and Tzeng [53], Yuan and Yu [38] and Zhu et al. [45] are based on asymmetric cryptography. A hybrid scheme integrating symmetric and public-key cryptography has been proposed by Lee and Lee et al. [54], exclusively for untrusted cloud environments. A scheme employing group signatures and homomorphic authentication code proposed by Wang et al. [9], supports the integrity verification of client data distributed among a large group of users.

2.2.7 Auditing mechanism

The kind of audit performed is an important characteristic for the classification of integrity verification schemes. Audit mechanisms are classified as public or private, based on the entities involved in the auditing process. Public auditing is performed by TPA or multiple users. On the other hand, data owners indulge in private auditing. Data leakage and user anonymity are significant security issues to be considered in the design of public auditing mechanisms. These schemes are further classified into privacy-preserving and non-privacy preserving mechanisms based on the disclosure of personal data during verification.

The Proof of Storage (POS) scheme proposed by Ateniese et al. [8] helps a client to get an assurance of a file residing in a particular server. It is a public audit scheme based on homomorphic authenticators. Similarly, the schemes proposed by Lee and Chang [54], Krzywiecki and Kutyłowski [11] and Shacham and Waters [49] are public auditing schemes. The scheme in [49] is implemented for handling large user groups without anydegradation in the performance of the verification process.

The auditing mechanism proposed by Shen and Tzeng [53], provides freedom to the client for delegating the auditing authority. A privacy-preserving scheme proposed by Nabeel and Bertino [55] defines access control mechanisms for storage as a service model. A thorough review of the security issues with public auditing has been presented by Wang et al., [51].

The private auditing scheme for assuring privacy in Database as a Service (DaaS) proposed by Alzain and Pardede [56] employs multiple data shares allowing the clients to ensure the correctness of data stored in the database.

Most auditing schemes are public in nature when the client data size is large. Private auditing schemes are suitable for private clouds where the anonymity of the user and the data must be maintained.

2.2.8 Data structures

Data or metadata cannot be directly accessed for verification from the storage as the client data blocks have varying sizes. The data structures employed in the representation of client data is attributed to the efficiency of the verification process. Hence, this is an important factor for the classification of integrity verification schemes. Efficient traversal algorithms simplify the searching and retrieval process, increasing the speed of verification. Further, the reorganization of the data after deletion operations minimizes the size of client data and the number of searches subsequently. Balanced trees are employed in many integrity verification schemes due to their ability to maintain a balanced height. Such a scheme has been proposed by Zhang and Blanton [40]. The Skip list data structure introduced by Pugh [57] demonstrates better performance compared to the balanced trees as it skips many blocks to reach the intended client block. The efficiency of skip lists in the creation of multidimensional indices for cloud data is demonstrated in the work of He et al. [116].

The MHT data structure was initially proposed by Merkle [58], in 1989,inthe construction of authentic digital signatures. This tree supports both authentication and integrity verification through the use of incremental computation of hash values, starting from the leaf nodes. The POR model proposed by Wang et al. [51] employs MHT for the construction of authentication tags for client data blocks. The use of homomorphic MHT in the streaming of authenticated data structures is seen in the work of Xu et al. [59].

2.3 PDP MODELS AND RELATED WORKS

Starting with the basic PDP proposed in [37], variants of PDP have been introduced recently, ensuring the assurance of the dynamic requirements of diverse client populations in integrated cloud computing environments. Followed by this model, the dual encryption-based PDP was proposed in [112]for the protection of the outsourced client data at the individual attribute levels. It employs RSA encryption for client data access with secret group keys generated from the attributes.

In mobile and cloud computing scenarios, clients place requests for sophisticated PDP services to the service providers. However, the PDP systems designed for conventional cloud-based solutions do not cater to the highly dynamic and resource-constrained devices in mobile computing environments. Mathematical computations for verification operations are performed by a TPA on behalf of mobile clients in the work of Yang et al. [60]. This scheme creates a small signature from a large client data file using MHT and bilinear signature, considerably minimizing overheads in communication and storage access.

In contrast to the traditional PDPs intended for static data, Dynamic PDPs (DPDP) proposed handle dynamic client operations. The earliest scheme proposed in [10], based on symmetric keys facilitates the dynamic modification, deletion and append operations on client data blocks for mobile devices. In continuation with this, an MHT and block tag authentication-based PDP scheme proposed in [19] by Wang et al. enables simultaneous auditing by multiple TPAs.

A two-phase scheme integrating MHT and Message Authentication Code (MAC) proposed by Shi et al. [17] also features dynamic integrity verification of client data. Following this, Erway et al. [10] have proposed a model similar to that of
[16] based on the construction of authentication dictionaries from rank information. Nevertheless, this scheme suffers from performance degradation when the file size increases.

In addition to authentication requirements, integrity and data availability of outsourced data are major security concerns for clients. These requirements are given due consideration in [41], in which mathematical computations are performed on both plain and encrypted data. Hash aggregation [113] schemes are encountered with security breaches during verification which is eliminated in [61] employing a rank based MHT.In this method, in addition to the hash value, each node is assigned a rank with respect to the frequency of operations on the corresponding data block, facilitating rapid access and retrieval of a particular node.

Non-repudiation is a major challenge to be handled with dishonest clients in cloud environments. A PDP model to confront this issue based on time-stamping is described in [62] which keeps track of the hash values to avoid synchronization problems. Similarly, a scheme to establish trust between clients and service providers is presented in [63] by Niaz and Saake et al., using radix path identifiers. A PDP scheme proposed in [64] by Peng et al., employs an authenticated skip list for quick retrieval of proof for data ownership and verification.

A majority of public audit schemes are designed as homomorphic schemes on sampled data blocks, which store block index information in tables. When the client data is subject to frequent updations, handling these tables is very difficult due to communication overheads. Data integrity verification can be performed rapidly using datastructures that facilitate faster retrieval of algorithms. Rank-based skip lists that demonstrate quick traversal and data retrieval can be used in realizing the properties such as public auditability, storage correctness, privacy, batch auditing, and data dynamics. These features have been demonstrated by the dynamic data verification systems proposed in [65] and [66].

2.4 MERKLE HASH TREE BASED PDPs

Data outsourced to cloud storage models implemented with weak security considerations are susceptible to side-channel attacks. An MHT based authentication model proposed in [67] by Koo et al. for preventing such attacksrenders the authentication proof unintelligible, such that it cannot be cracked by an adversary.

A similar scheme for the protection of the personal data of the client stored in multiple storage devices, proposed by Cho et al. [68] employs MACs and MHT for the construction of a reliable logging mechanism to trace the operations on personal records.

MHTs are commonly used data structures in the implementation of cryptographic algorithms. The correctness of client data, represented as a node of an MHT, can be verified using the hash value of the root node and the authentication path spanning the nodes from the root node to the leaf node. Traversal in an MHT refers to the identification of authentication paths for all the leaf nodes. The storage of each node in the path is unrealistic in multi-cloud environments due to client dynamics. Similarly, finding authentication paths for non-leaf nodes at the top of the tree is computationally expensive. The concept ofFMT was proposed by Jakobsson et al. [69], in progression to the fundamental hash chain traversal approaches proposed in [70,71] for overcoming these issues.

In the elementary hash chain traversal based cryptographic mechanisms, the final hash value computed from the initialization vector and the data blocks is of interest to the verifier. Nevertheless, the authentication paths and the hash values of the nodes along these paths are significant for the verifier in the performance of computations in the integrity check process. The client data blocks are accessed by either the data owner or multiple stakeholders in a multi-cloud environment based on the access control mechanisms enforced. This is akin to the access to the leaf nodes of the MHT representation of a large client data file. Confining the access to a leaf node, i.e. client data in an MHT, broadcasting mechanisms to reach multiple clients and security protocols to counter wormhole attacks with malicious nodes are implemented in [72,73]. These mechanisms are extended in [74,75] for robust micro-payment procedures and secured revocation of public authentication certificates. Similarly, digital signatures of client data files are created by providing privileges to access multiple client data blocks.

The above services can be realized with FMTs with low storage and computational complexities. The FMT is a minimal representation of a tree that maintains only the essential nodes for computations and discards the others. This fractal representation results in FMTs exhibiting very low computational and storage complexities compared to the basic MHT.

Knecht et al. [76] have presented a detailed analysis of the complexities of MHTs and proposed novel algorithms, throughan effective coupling of the space-time trade-off featured in [77] with the space conservation mechanism of [78], realizing space minimization by 50 % compared to the fundamental algorithm in [77].

In the basic hash chain operations, the client data blocks, all of which are uniformly sized are iteratively hashed. This results in asymptotic running times, with linear variations with the number of client data blocks. However, these operations do not suitmulti-cloud environments, in which the size of the client data block varies from time to time. These issues can be resolved using FMTs with parallel hashing techniques proposed in [79], for resource-constrained devices.

Further, variants of the modes of hash tree representations are evaluated in [80], with due consideration of resource utilization problems in parallel computing. Parallel hashing techniques are implemented using MHTs, by assigning the hashing operations to multiple processors and employing a unique processor to hash the concatenation of hash sequences incrementally. Integrity verification mechanisms implemented on FMTs with parallel hashing are faster than that of MHT based schemes.

FMTs employ a process called scheduling for unambiguous selection of the next node for computation, without sacrificing the recent modifications in the data blocks. Hence, FMTsare good replacements for MHTs in the construction of cryptosystems for digital signature generation, proof generation, authentication and integrity verification.

Naor et al. [62] have introduced a one-time signature scheme called

FMTseq,which is faster than the asymmetric digital signature schemes. The performance realized with this approach has motivated the implementation of several security solutions based on MHTs and its variants. Further, MHTs are also used in digital forensic applications in the generation of digital evidence faster as described in Berbecaru [81].

The PMT with improved capabilities, representing eachnode as a 3-tuple was introduced recently, as an add-on to the existing MHTs. In a PMT, each node is aware of its position relative to other nodes in the tree. In the pioneering work of Mao et al. [82], the first publicly verifiable integrity verification scheme based on challenge-response model, employing PMT has been proposed. This scheme has been extended by the authors in [83] for verification of sensitive data captured from sensors in a heterogeneous multi-cloud environment.

Unauthorized access to data can be prevented by tracking the usage profile of clients in a cloud. Intrusion detection mechanisms and statistical models are employed in digital forensics for creating usage trails and raising security alerts. Basically, public auditing systems proposed in [84], create user logs for tracing the origin of security attacks with low overheads. Further, as an extension to the above, binary auditing trees have been employed in [85] for data integrity protection, client-side non-repudiation detection, log file verification, source of attack localization, etc.

Client data are also susceptible to internal attacks and lack of updation of all replicas, which are significant threats to the integrity of the service provider. These attacks are addressed in the work of Levitin et al. [86] and probabilistic models have been used formodelling the behaviour of genuine clients and attackers for detection and localization of attacks and adversaries.

Cloud infrastructures are vandalized by attackers due to the presence of breaches in the implementation of security mechanisms. This can be avoided by rendering the generation of counterfeit proofs and cracking the authentic proofs computationally difficult. In the MHT based scheme of Koo et al. [67], the data ownership proof is encrypted for preventing guessing attacks. Similarly, the likelihood of attacks increases with the distribution of multiple replicas of client data across cloud storage devices. The integrity verification schemes based on group keys proposed by Cho et al. [68] are used for verification of data in a distributed cloud environment.

Further, the protection of data in distributed databases in dynamic environments with multiple database clients is a highly challenging problem, with the additional requirement to satisfy performance requirements. The Bayesian theorem-based data model proposed in [87] has demonstrated the provision of security services, also ensuring thebest QoS.

Low-cost integrity verification mechanisms similar to the one proposed in [68], based on MACs for resource-constrained mobile devices can be realized with MHTs. In cloud environments, solution methodologies should be selected after a thorough assessment of client requirements, capabilities of infrastructure, deployment intricacies, etc. as suggested in [88]. This very well applies to the MHT based integrity verification schemes, as variants of MHT feature different properties individually and when coupled with other methods.

In cloud environments, adversariesinterfere with the computations outsourced by the clients, compromisingthe reliability of the service providers. Data owners must be assured of non-performance of unauthorized computations on the data with robust and less complex security mechanisms as in [89].

A review of cryptographic systems shows modular arithmetic operations as central to security mechanisms, due to the computational complexity seen in them. Modular exponentiation operations in the integrity verification process are outsourced by resource-constrained client devices. Such schemes are proposed in [67] and [90] are those in which low computationally intensive operations are performed by the client withthe simultaneous performance of modular exponentiations by the server.

In addition to the generic security mechanisms, specific [63] security provisions are also offered based on client requirements. Such mechanisms customized to the client requirements include attribute-based encryption for the protection of sensitive data, fine-grained access control to specific fields of client data records, restricting the number of users, number of accesses to certain data, etc. Stringent requirements of this kind can be realized with well-defined tracking mechanisms employing MHTs.

Clients are highly apprehensive of revealing sensitive data to TPAs for auditing. Further, retrieval of the entire client data for verification is also impractical and poses severe security threats. The integration of homomorphic schemes with MHTs averts this problem as verification operations are performed on encrypted data by the verifier as in [64].

With the transformation of healthcare service models to the cloud, large volumes of client data are maintained in heterogeneous multi-cloud environments. Integration of the Internet of Things (IoT) with a cloud environment simplifies data acquisition and manipulation of clinical data. But it also features severe security risks when the security mechanisms are not robust. Cloud-based healthcare services are in practice as described in the works of Elhoseny et al. [90] and Bai et al. [91,92].

Security mechanisms designed for these services must be less vulnerable and flexible, ensuring the simultaneous availability of services. Such solutions can be designed only with data structures that feature faster traversal algorithms, reorganization capabilities, selective retrieval, indexing, awareness on the dynamics of client data, etc. With the demonstrated abilities of MHTs and variants, they are found highly suitable for the construction of PDPs for dynamic verification of sensitive client data. A consolidated timeline diagram shown in Figure 2.2 highlights the features incorporated in the data integrity verification mechanisms proposed so far.

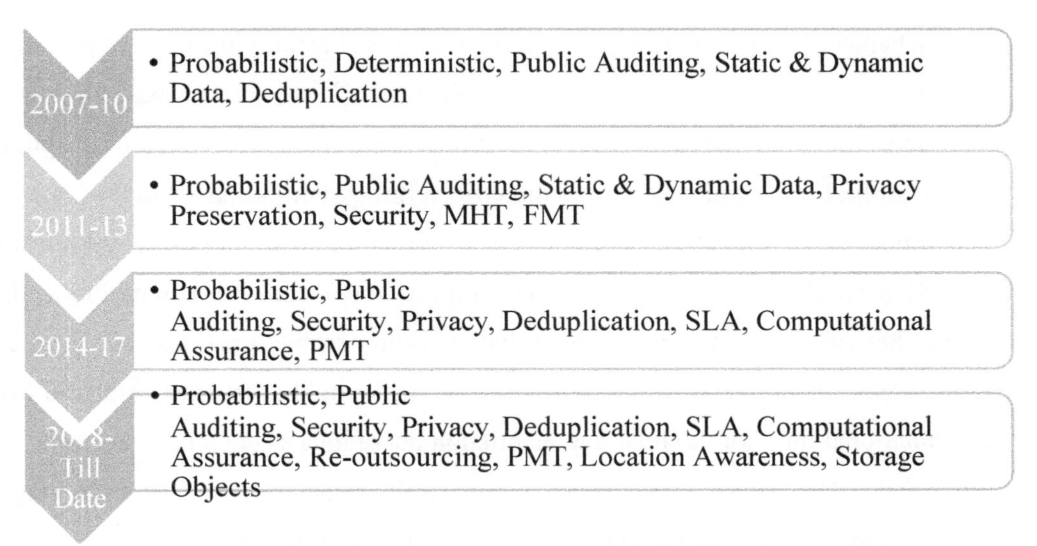

Figure 2.2 Data Integrity Verification Mechanism Timeline

2.5 HOMOMORPHIC ENCRYPTION AND ITS RELATED WORKS

Homomorphic Encryption (HE) is a kind of encryption that permits mathematical computations on encrypted data, protecting the original data. This concept called privacy homomorphism was introduced in [93] to perform a large set of mathematical operations on encrypted data. Fully Homomorphic Encryption (FHE) refers to an encryption function that permits multiple operations on encrypted data. The earliest homomorphic scheme based on lattice computations was proposed by Gentry [94]. The security of this system was enhanced through the use of bootstrapping which generates distinct ciphertexts for every encryption of the same plain text as illustrated in [95]. Later, the scheme proposed in [94] was extended by Dijk et al. [96], in which computations are performed on integers. Further, bootstrapping schemes that minimize the noise in the ciphertext have also been proposed for a reduction in the influence of noise in the multiple ciphertexts constructed from a single plain text.

FHE schemes are classified on the basis of the encryption mechanisms employed. FHE functions homomorphic for a single operation on client data are called partial

FHE schemes. The asymmetric RSA cryptosystem [97] employing a pair of private and public keys, which facilitates the multiplication of two ciphertexts, is partially homomorphic. The product of plain texts is recovered on the decryption of the product of two ciphertexts. Similarly, the asymmetric cryptosystem proposed in [98] is a PHE in addition. Somewhat HE (SHE) is a kind of homomorphism proposed by Melchor et al. [99], for addition and multiplication operations with a constraint on multiplication.

Further enhancements of the integer-based homomorphic functions have been done by reducing the public key size. Minimization of the public key size results in lower computational time for modular exponentiation operations as demonstrated in [100] and [101]. Further, the concept of downscaling the ciphertext for improving the speed of the modular exponentiation operations has been proposed in [102].

The security of a cryptographic system depends on the difficulty in inversion, i.e., the computational complexity involved in the reconstruction of the secret message from the ciphertext. This recovery model called Learning with Errors (LWE), based on solving simultaneous linear equations,has been proposed in [103]. An improved version of this scheme has been presented for fine-grained encryption in [104]. Similarly, the basic model proposed in [103] has been extended to operate on matrices in [105], considerably reducing the computational cost.

From an elaborate review on the HE schemes, it is evident that FHE schemes are best suited for the implementation of PDPs, in the establishment of trust among stakeholders in heterogeneous environments, for the deployment of successful business models. Security concerns in cloud-based enterprise solutions are very well explored in [108] and security mechanisms built on HE are highly recommended to address the security and privacy challenges in client data outsourcing.

In highly controlled environments such as banking and finance, healthcare, defence, etc., HE schemes facilitate the creation of new services eliminating privacy concerns. Privacy though refers to data privacy in general, is also associated with the seclusion of certain aspects of the enterprise models such as system functionalities, data queries, access privileges with the server, storage access, client-side behaviours, etc. Despite immense care taken in ensuring the privacy of data, emphasis not given to other privacy requirements even at the policy level of organizations is not much to speak of.

FHE schemes with a good degree of freedom to perform operations on encrypted data are highly indispensable in the realization of enterprise solution architectures which can be tailored to different functional domains. Further, in major verticals such as healthcare and finance with a large client population, protection of data along with the transactions is very crucial, with no performance compromises. The FHE scheme proposed by Asharov et al. [107] features low overheads in cloud environments characterized by multiple entities with diverse privacy requirements.

Business models implemented in the cloud exhibit different internal functionalities and provide well-defined interfaces to the clients to utilize the solutions. Care must be taken to ensure that the operations performed by the client on data are not disclosed to unauthorized users. Naehrig et al. [108] have demonstrated the accomplishment of this requirement with HE schemes based on algebraic computations with matrices.

Similarly, it has been shown in [109] that privacy on data and query can both be simultaneously realized with HE based verification schemes. Data leakage, i.e. the disclosure of data to unauthorized entities in the cloud environment is a common issue due to the maintenance of multiple replicas of client data and the transition between private and public clouds in a hybrid cloud environment.

This problem has been investigated in [110] and HE of client data before outsourcing has been advocated as a promising solution. The potential of public-key cryptosystems in the design of security mechanisms for data confidentiality, digital signature generation and verification, integrity checks, authentication, and shared computations has been demonstrated by numerous researchers. These mechanisms can be further enhanced by protecting the data by FHE schemes.

2.6 SUMMARY

A detailed review of relevant literatureshows the security requirements in cloud-based environments as veryrigorous, and, at the same time, flexibility in services is the major client-side requirement. It is understood that client-side requirements in turn call for strict security policies addressing access control mechanisms, number, and frequency of data accesses, attribute-based access, etc. Security-flexibility trade-offs are the most significant concern in the design of security mechanisms. It is evident that MHT based methods demonstrate the desired qualities of cryptographic systems such as quick traversal, retrieval, and ease of computations. Similarly, FHE schemes are identified for the protection of client data from unauthorized access. Hence, these approaches can be eventually employed for realizing the objectives of this research and they are fundamental to the various PDPs implemented in this research.

This section consummates a detailed review ofthe literaturerelated to the topic of this research works, identifying the requirements of contemporary cloud-based systems, contributions of researchers, limitations of the existing approaches and emphasizing the need for the proposed research.

CHAPTER 3

SKIP LIST AND MERKLE HASH TREE BASED DYNAMIC PROVABLE DATA POSSESSION MODEL FOR MULTI-CLOUD

3.1 INTRODUCTION

In recent years, enterprises provide highly interactive business models in several domains for diverse clients, irrespective of geographical locations, ensuring the availability of reliable solutions. Many business models are designed on processing historical data archived in cloud storage devices and dynamic real-time data, frequently accessed by various entities in the workflow. Data security services that ensurethe integrity of data are highly essential for cloud-based enterprise applications in which clients demand proof of data security. Of late, the multi-cloud environment has captivated theinterest of the clients due to the versatility of services offered by different providers under a single platform. This version of the cloud seamlessly integrates services from numerous hosts with the frequent switch over and load balancing capabilities for enhanced customer experience. Proofof data ownership and integrity check mechanisms are very stringent in multi-cloud [88] due to the high level of data dynamics.

Recently, many healthcare providers have adopted multi cloud-based solution models to reach remote destinations. The static and dynamic data owned by healthcare providers require protection from intentional and unintentional attacks during retrieval. Most importantly, the data owners and clients require the assurance of the data not being tampered. This is possible through the use of strong integrity check mechanisms without compromising the quality of service. This section presents a model for establishing data ownership and integrity verification in a multi-cloud environment using two data structures namely the skip list and the Merkle tree. This model has been implemented and tested in a multi-cloud environment. The following subsections provide a succinct background of the model and its mathematical foundations.

3.1.1 Provable Data Possession

The explosion in digital content and flexibility of cloud computing has led to a great demand for data storage. Remote storage of data is popular among consumers due to cost-effectiveness and access flexibility. However, consumers are confronted with critical issues related to the storage and retrieval of data from remote servers. More particularly, they demand proof for security [111] of their data from storage outsourcing services providers. It is essential for commercial service providers to demonstrate the integrity of consumer data placed in untrusted remote servers. A PDP model enables a client in the verification of its data filekept in an untrusted remote server as intact without extracting the entire file. The following are the essential features of any PDP.

- Public verification.
- An unconstrained number of verifications.
- On the fly data updation.
- Conservation of storage and computing resources.
- The efficiency of algorithms.

A generic PDP protocol involves four steps, namely, pre-processing, inquiry, confirmation and check. Initially, a client pre-processes its data/file to be shared for the generation of small metadata and stores it locally. The client then sends the file to the server and deletes its copy. Inquiry refers to the process of sending a random challenge by the client to the server. Based on the client data saved in the remote storage, the server calculates the response to the challenge and transmits it to the client. This response is compared with the metadata by the client ensuring the data in the remote storage devicesis secure. PDP protocol is classified as public and private verifiable based on the verification entities. In a private-check PDP, the data owner alone can verify the data in a server, while in a public or multiple checkPDP, any authorized entity does that.

Basically, PDP can be implemented using a hash function. Initially, a clientcomputes a set of k challenges c_i, $i \in \{1,k\}$. For each challenge, the client computes the proof p_i by hashing the challenge c_i concatenated with the original data D as $H(c_i || D)$. The client randomly sends c_i to the server and requests the server to solve it. The server, in turn, computes p_i' as $H(c_i || D)$ and returns it to the client. The client compares p_i and p_i' and ensures the data is intact with the server if $p_i = p_i'$. This procedure is given as a PDP algorithm in Figure 3.1.

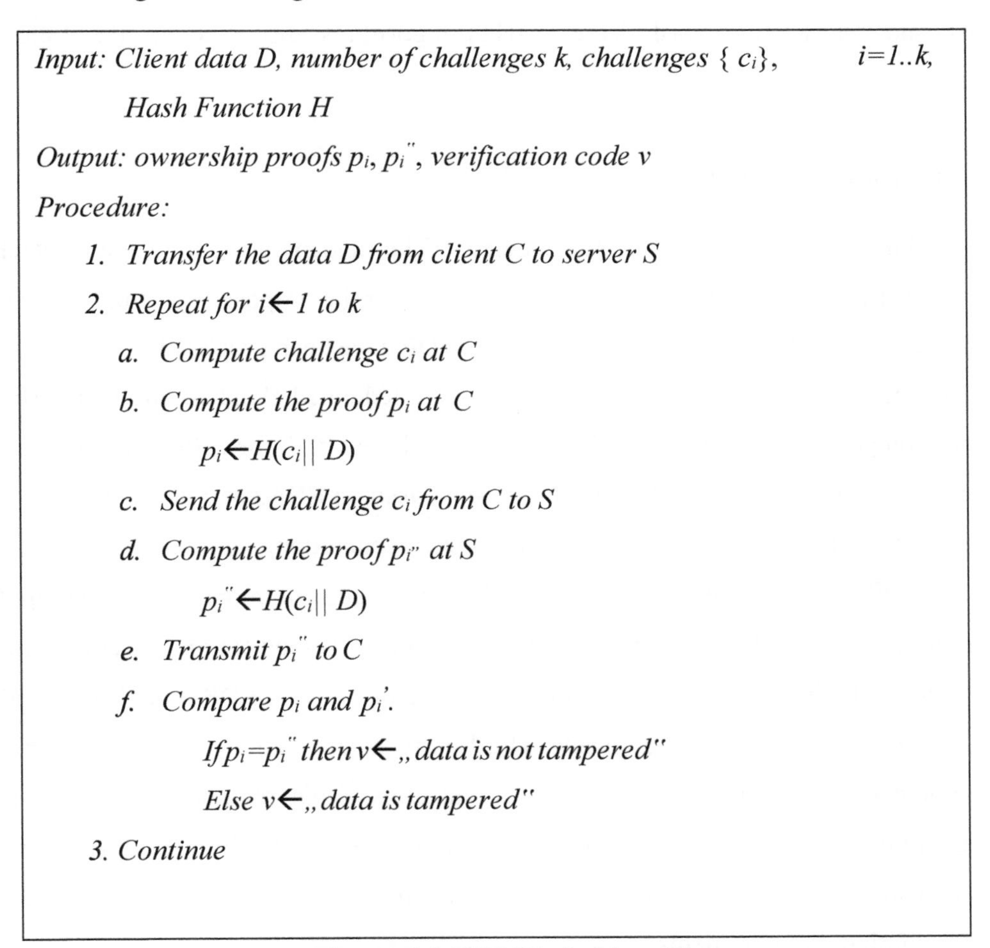

Input: Client data D, number of challenges k, challenges $\{ c_i \}$, $i=1..k$,

Hash Function H

Output: ownership proofs p_i, p_i'', *verification code v*

Procedure:

1. *Transfer the data D from client C to server S*
2. *Repeat for* $i \leftarrow 1$ *to k*
   a. *Compute challenge* c_i *at C*
   b. *Compute the proof* p_i *at C*
      $p_i \leftarrow H(c_i || D)$
   c. *Send the challenge* c_i *from C to S*
   d. *Compute the proof* p_i'' *at S*
      $p_i'' \leftarrow H(c_i || D)$
   e. *Transmit* p_i'' *to C*
   f. *Compare* p_i *and* p_i'.
      If $p_i = p_i''$ *then* $v \leftarrow$ *„data is not tampered"*
      Else $v \leftarrow$ *„data is tampered"*
3. *Continue*

Figure 3.1 PDP Hash Algorithm

This approach limits the number of challenges to k with the additional requirements of the retrieval of the data D from the server, every time a challenge is sent by the client. This process suffers from I/O overheads due to the retrieval of data from the server. The earliest PDP model was proposed by Ateniese et al. [37].It provides a probabilistic proof for storage of file by a third party. Unlike the conventional PDP, this approach accesses only small data chunks of a file for proof of ownership. The PDP based data integrity verification can be simplified using the skip list and the Merkle Hash Tree (MHT) algorithms discussed in the following subsections.

3.2 RELATED WORK

This section presents a detailed review of the fundamental and recent research in the construction of PDPs and advocates the need for the proposed system. With the introduction ofPDP in [37], new versions of PDP have been proposed to date featuring the dynamic needs of diverse clients in federated cloud environments.Hur and Noh [112] have proposed a dual encryption-based PDP for enforcing fine-grained access control in outsourced data. This model based on RSA encryption facilitates data management with attribute-based group key generation.

PDP services are in great demand from clients in mobile cloud computing environments. The PDP systems intended for traditional cloud computing environments are not suitable for resource-constrained mobile devices. A PDP model proposed by Yang et al. [60] employs a trusted Third-party aGent (TPG), which performs the mathematical computations for mobile end-users. This method employs bilinear signature and MHT in the construction of a small signature by the aggregation of verification tokens generated from large client data files, reducing storage and computational requirements.

Contrary to the conventional PDP models for static data, Dynamic Provable Data Possession (DPDP)models have been proposed for handling dynamic changes to data. Ateniese et al. [36] have introduced a PDP for mobile devices employing a symmetric key, which supports block modification, deletion and append operations dynamically. Similarly, a PDP scheme based on MHT and block tag authentication to address the security issues in dynamic data updation in remote storage deviceshave been proposed by Wang et al. [113]. Their approach also supports simultaneousmultiple auditing by the TPAs. Stefanov et al. [114] have proposed a two-layer authentication scheme which is a combination of Message Authentication Code (MAC) and MHT for dynamic data integrity verification of data blocks of client files. Later, Erway et al. [10], constructing authentication dictionaries from rank information, have proposed a model similar to [36]. However, a performance degradation from $O(1)$ to $O(log\ n)$ was observed for dynamic verification of data for a data fileof n blocks.

Ensuring the correctness and availability of the cloud data transferred between untrusted clouds is also a major concern for clients. This issue is addressed in [115] and the proposed approach has the ability to perform operations on both plain text and encrypted text. In this approach, proof forpossession and deletion of data can be generated from two clouds involved, irrespective of whether the data is encrypted or not. The security flaws seen during hash aggregation in [113] are analyzed and a ranked MHT based PDP has been proposed in [61]. In this approach, a pair of values comprising the hash code and rank value is assigned to each node. The rank is computed on the basis of operations performed on the data block corresponding to the node, which helps to trackthe operations performed on a block.

A non-repudiable PDP model integrating time-stamping with MHT for handling dishonest clients has been presented in [87]. This method obviates synchronization problems and tampering of stored hash values and cloud returned values. An MHT based authentication scheme employing Radix Path Identifiers to enforce trust between data owners and service providers has been presented by Niaz and Saake in [63]. Cloud data integrity verification is implemented in large scale data storage using authenticated skip lists that store the sorted membership proofs. Efficiency in the extraction of proof for the client data from the list is very important for quick verification. An algorithm for the implementation of an authenticated skip list has been proposed by Peng et al. [64].

Most of the public auditing schemes for remote integrity verification of outsourced data are based on homomorphic encryption and random block sampling.They havethe need to maintain tables for handling the block index information. However, the management of tables is difficult when the outsourced data is updated frequently. The use of rank-based skip lists eliminates the need for these tables and simplifies data integrity verification. These data structures are designed to provide the features of public auditability, the correctness of data in storage, privacy, batch auditing, and data dynamics. Stability seen in rank-based skip lists leads to their use in building dynamic integrity verification systems as evident from [65,66].

Weak cloud storage frameworks are prone to faceside-channel attacks on online data. A novel MHT based authentication model has been proposed by Koo et al. [67] exclusively for securing online data by modifying the authentication proof such that, it cannot be broken by an attacker. An integrity check mechanism to verify the intactness of personal information stored across multiple storage devices has been proposed by Cho et al. [68]. It features a reliable logging mechanism based on MACs and MHT to track access to personal records.

3.3 PROPOSED METHODOLOGY

A detailed review of PDP models in the previous section leads to the understanding of the MHT and skip list based integrity verification systems as very effective in dynamic cloud environments. An elaboratedepiction of the underlying methodologies employed in the proposed system is presented in this section.

3.3.1 Skip List

A skip list [57] is a data structure that stores sorted items in the form of multiple hierarchical linked lists. Each node in the skip list has 4 pointers, (*left, right, bottom* and *top*)pointing to the 4 neighbours. The linked lists at the higher level of the hierarchy are sparser compared to those at the bottom levels. This structure simplifies data search and insertion. A skip list with four levels of hierarchy is shown in Figure.3.2.

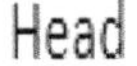

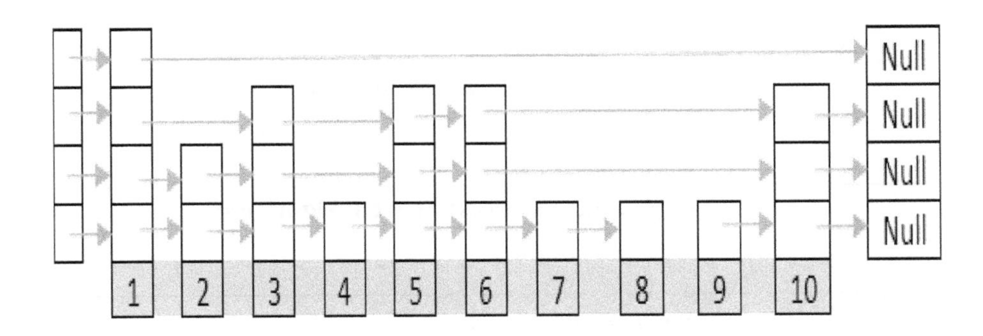

Figure 3.2 Skip List

Skip lists have a search and insertion complexity of *O*(*log n*)due to the simplicity of these processes. These operations proceed from the highest level of hierarchy to the bottom level, traversing each linked list until the required element is found or inserted. These lists are called skip lists as many sub-sequences are skipped in the searching process. The skip list search and insertion algorithms are shown in Figure 3.3 and 3.4 respectively. These algorithms depict only the adjacent nodes affected during insertion of a new element and, the entire list need not be traversedfor searching operations. Due to these features, skip lists are used in the construction of distributed systems where each computer system is represented with a node in a skip list and network connection is represented with a pointer. Skip lists are found to be better replacements for balanced trees for several applications as proved by Pugh [57].

Input: Skip list L, element to be inserted elm
Output: insertion location of element loc
Procedure:

1. *l←search(elm)*
2. *loc←insert_after(l,elm)*
3. *h←1*
4. *Repeat for each elm*
   a. *h←h+1*
   b. *if (h>L.Height)create_newlevel()*
   c. *l←l.top*
   d. *loc= insert_after(l,elm)*
5. *Continue*
6. *Increment the number of elements in the list*
   a. *n←n+1*
   b. *return loc*

Figure 3.3 Skip List Search Algorithm

Input: Skip list L, element to search elm

Output: location of element loc

Procedure:

1. *loc←top_left_node(L)*
2. *while (loc.bottom!=NULL)*
   a. *if loc.right> elm*
      i. *loc←loc.bottom*
   b. *else if (loc.bottom<=elm)*
      i. *loc←loc.right*
3. *return loc*

Figure 3.4 Skip List Insertion Algorithm

Skip lists find applications in several computational frameworks in distributed computing environments such as Apache Portable Runtime (APR), Cyrus IMAP server, Lucence, etc. In cloud storage which manages data with multidimensional [116] data structures, skip lists are used for simplification of the search and retrieval process.

3.3.2 Merkle Hash Tree (MHT)

MHT [89] is a tree data structure, a generalization of hash lists. In an MHT, each leaf node is assigned a label, which is the hash value computed from the data block represented by it. Node labels for non-leaf nodes are created by hashing the labels of the respective child nodes. The MHTs are used for verification of large volumes of data distributed across multiple storage nodes in distributed storage environments. MHT is employed in the authentication frameworks for cloud storage. The client data block can be assigned a signature generated using an MHT and subsequently verified to ensure the integrity of client data.

Generally, the client file is represented as a collection of data blocks each of which is verified with a one-way hash function. Each leaf node of an MHT corresponds to a client data block and is assigned a hash value computed from the data block. The hash labels of the leaf nodes are concatenated and hashed incrementally to construct a hash tree. The root node of the tree is assigned a label which is the hash value of the concatenated hash labels of the subtrees. Figure 3.5 shows an MHT with four-leaf nodes *m1, m2, m3,* and *m4*.

Initially, each of these nodes is hashed for obtaining the hash values $h(m1)$, $h(m2)$, $h(m3)$ and $h(m4)$. Then, $h(m1)$ and $h(m2)$ are hashed together to get h_a. Similarly, *m3* and *m4* and are hashed to h_b. Finally, $h_a$andh_b are hashed together to h_r. i.e., $h_r = h(h_a || h_b)$.

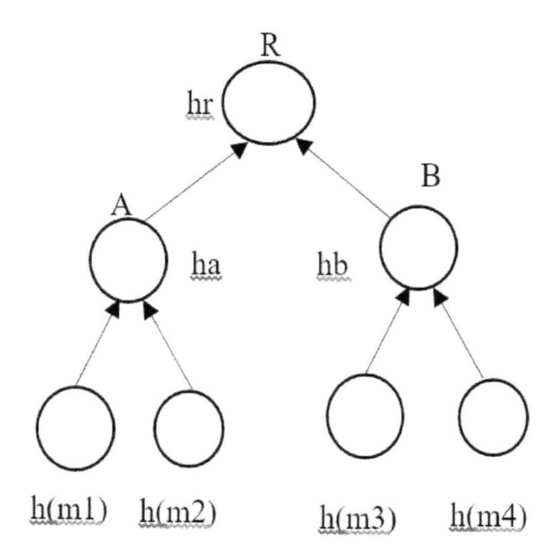

Figure 3.5 Merkle Hash Tree

In storage outsourcing infrastructures, multiple copies of data are distributed across storage nodes. If data is modified by the client, the changes require reflection in all the copies. It is very difficult to verify the entire data contents in all the locations. This process is simplified with the MHT based verification protocol as shown in Figure 3.6. It is based on the conjecture of the creationof MHT for the client data fileshared with the server at the client with both the data and MHT sent to the server. This protocol does not require the transfer of the entire file for verification. Only the hash values are transferred among the client and the server for verification.

Input: Client file F, Hash Function H

Output: verification code v

Procedure:

1. *Construct the MHT M for F*

   M←MHT(F)

2. *Transfer F and M from client C to server S*
3. *Construct a hash of the File at C and send it to S*
   a. *H(F)→S*
4. *Initialize N with the root node N←M.root*
5. *Repeat for all nodes starting with N*
   a. *Verify the hash value with the hash value of N at S*

      If (H(F)=N.Hash

      i. *Return v←„data is not tampered"*

      Else

      i. *request for hash values of subtrees of N*
      ii. *Return v←„data is tampered"*
6. *Continue*

Figure 3.6 MHT based Data Verification Protocol

Merkle [89] employed this data structure for the creation of a digital signature of a file to be exchanged, as an alternative to the conventional encryption system. Introduced in 1989, MHT and its variants are used widely in the recent cryptographic systems, thanks to its scalable block-based verification which is most desirable in the implementation of granular data verification systems.

3.4 ARCHITECTURE OF PROPOSED METHODOLOGY

A description of the architecture of the proposed PDP, based on both MHT and skip list with algorithms for integrity verification and experimental results has been provided in the subsections that follow.

3.4.1 Dynamic PDP Architecture

The schematic of the proposed system is shown in Figure 3.7. The data owners represent the file F to be shared as a set of n blocks $\{b_1,b_2...b_n\}$ done with the server to be stored in the cloud. The client maintains a skip list L and stores the blocks at the bottom of the list. The node r at the top of the list contains the number of nodes at the bottom list reachable from r. It makes the search for a data block easier with the skip list. The client maintains an array A to keep track of the number of updations in each block. From each block b_i, key $k_i$is generated; further, from each key k_i, a tag $t_i$is generated by applying the Merkle hash function H. The key and the tag sequences are maintained by the server using arrays.

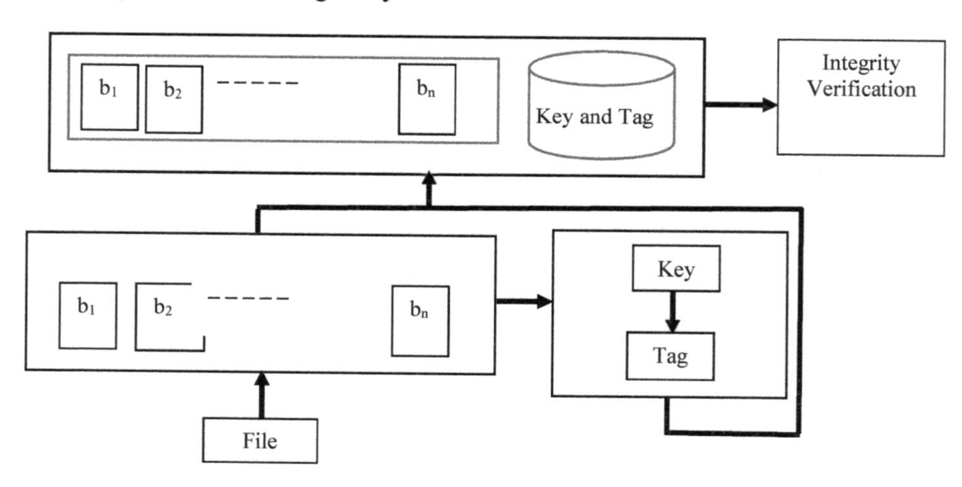

Figure 3.7 Dynamic PDP

The protocol architecture of the proposed system consists of the following functions.

***KeyGen*(p_k,s_k)**

This is a key generation function run by the client initially, for the creation ofa public and secret key pair for asymmetric cryptographic operations between the client and server.

***TagBlock*(p_k,s_k, *m*)**

The client executes this function to generate metadatafrom the data file for verification and to assign tags to file blocks for integrity verification.

***GenProof*(p_k, *F*,*chal*, $\sum$)**

This function is invoked by the server to create a proof for a data owned by a client.

***CheckProof*(p_k,s_k,*chal*, *V*)$\rightarrow${*success*, *failure*}**

This function is executed by the client to enable verification of the proofgenerated at the server matching with that of the client.The algorithms for building the above functions are discussed in the next section.

3.4.2 Key, Tag and Merkle Tree Generation

The process of generation of Keys, Tags and the Merkle trees begins with the representation of each block as a sequence of lines of uniform length. The key sequence k_1, k_2...$k_n$is formed by combining the first characters of the lines.On each key k_i, the Merkle Hash function is applied to generate the tag value t_i.The hash function H is applied on the tag sequence t_1, t_2...$t_n$iteratively to generate the MHT. The skip list L is created to maintain the nodes of the trees for faster access. The algorithm for the generation of key and tag sequences and the Merkle tree is given in Figure 3.8.

Input: Client file F, Hash Function H

Output: key sequence $k_1, k_2 \ldots k_n$, tag sequence $t_1, t_2 .. t_n$, Merkle Hash Tree M

Procedure:

1. *Divide F in to equal sized blocks $b_1, b_2 \ldots b_n$*

//Key and Tag sequence Generation

2. *Repeat for each block b_i*
    a. *Extract the first character c_1 from b_i for each line l_i*
        i. $c_1 \leftarrow firstchar(l_i)$
        ii. *Append c_1 iteratively to k_i*

            $k_i \leftarrow k_i || c_1$
    b. *Apply the Hash function on k_i to generate t_i*

        $t_i \leftarrow H(k_i)$
3. *Continue*

//Merkle Tree Generation

4. *M.Root =NULL*
5. $i \leftarrow 1$
6. *Repeat for each t_i and t_{i+1}*
    a. $h_i \leftarrow H(t_i || t_{i+1})$
    b. $i \leftarrow i+2$
    c. $h_{i+1} \leftarrow H(t_i || t_{i+1})$
    d. *M.LTree* $\leftarrow h_i$
    e. *M.RTree* $\leftarrow h_{i+1}$
7. *Continue*

Figure 3.8Algorithm for Key, Tag and Merkle Tree Generation

3.4.3 Integrity Verification Process

A detailed description of the integrity verification process for the insertion, deletion and updation operations is provided in this section. Modification of any data blockb_i is reflected in the respective key k_i and tag t_i and updated by the client. Integrity checks can be performed for insertion, deletion and modification operations by the client. The client submits a request for integrity verification to the server and receives the response and compares it with tag values.If the tag values are different, the particular block b_i can be localized. Further, the tampered data in the block can be identified,through a comparison of the key values, as such values are dependent on the content of the data block.

Insertion

On insertion of a new block $b_{n+1}$to the skip list, the client expands the array $A$of size n to $n+1$ and computes the key k_{n+1} and the tag $t_{n+1}$and sends these data to the server. A new noder_i is inserted into the hash tree $M$and in the skip list L. It is added in the bottom-most level at the appropriate location to maintain L as a sorted list. Now, the new hash value is computed appending $t_{n+1}$and its sibling and the hash value of its parent is modified without affecting the rest of the tree.

Deletion

On the deletion of a new block b_i,the client sends the block index $i$to the server. The client then searches for the skip list L and deletes b_i. It also deletes the key $k_i$and the tag t_i. The client then updates the hash value in M and deletes the element corresponding to the deleted block b_i. The client then sends the modified hash value and a randomly generated key for the verification of the successful completion of the deletion operation.

Updation

In order to edit the contents of a block $b_i$in the server, the client sends the block index $i$to the server. The server retrieves b_i from the skip list L and transfers the tuple $\{b_i, k_i, t_i\}$ containing the block, key and tag values to the client. At the client-side, an integrity check is performed at the client-side and the block content is updated. Now the new values of $k_i$and$t_i$are computed and the modified tuple $\{b_i, k_i, t_i\}$ is forwarded to the server. The skip list L and the hash code of the modified node in $M$are updated by the server. Finally, the client sends a random key and hash value and verifies the integrity of the data after updation of the block contents.

3.5 EXPERIMENTAL RESULTS AND DISCUSSIONS

3.5.1 Experimental Setup

Focusing on the evolution of the medical cloud to provide healthcare services to remote end-users, the researcher has tested the system proposed by him in a healthcare multi-cloud. The proposed system wasdeployed and tested in a multi- cloud setting configured using a Cloud Simulator, Google drive, a DropBox and Cloud Me. The protocol for data integrity check was implemented with algorithms for the generation of keys, tags, proof and verification codes, implemented in Java with Eclipse as the front end. The proposed system was implemented and tested in two different environments.

The mathematical computations are based on the public and secret key pairs. These key pairs are generated from the key associated with data block. The size of the public and private keys is fixed as 160 bits [137] in our experiments.

In the first, the performance of the proposed algorithm using both skip list and MHT was compared with the MHT algorithm on an exclusive dataset, to demonstrate the efficacy of the algorithm in a multi-cloud environment, for proof generation and verification. This environment createdwas simulated with a Cloud Simulator (CloudSim) and Elastic Utility Computing Architecture for Linking Your Programs to Useful Systems (EUCALYPTUS), a free software implemented in Java and C which facilitatedthe expansion of the cloud to accommodate low and high client population. In the second, the system was tested in a multi-cloud environment on dynamic insertion, deletion and updation operations and the results were compared with those obtained in a single cloud environment.

The multi-cloud setup for the experimental works is shown in Figure 3.9. This arrangement is realized with a collection of cloud nodes in the with Walrus. It provides persistent storage to the Virtual Machines in the Eucalyptus cloud and also offers a solution similar to HTTP get/put solution model.

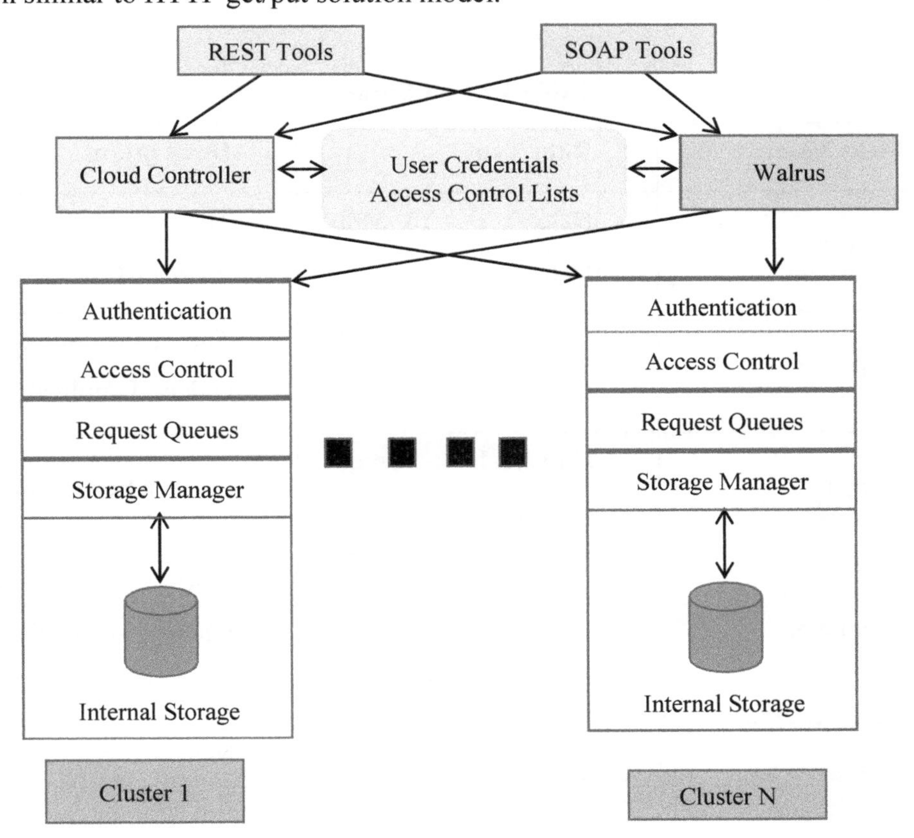

Figure 3.9 Multi-cloud Architecture for Dynamic PDP

3.5.2 Test data and Use cases

The algorithms were tested using a file containing 512 synthetic health care records, created with the open-source Synthea software which models synthetic patient records. Secure Hash Algorithm (SHA)-512 was used for hashing.The performance of the algorithm was tested for insertion, deletion and updation operations on the patient records. Synthea supportedthe creation of patient data as Comma Separated Value (CSV) formats for various dictionaries such as allergies, encounters, conditions, observations, medications, etc. In this experiment, the medications dictionary was selected for testing thealgorithms proposed by the researcher. The structure of the records is shown in Table 3.1.

Table 3.1Test Dataset Structure

Field Name	Data Type	Description
DeStart	Date (YYYY-MM-DD)	The date the medication was prescribed.
Stop	Date (YYYY-MM-DD)	The date the prescription ended, if applicable.
Patient	Universal Unique Identifier(UUID)	Foreign key to the Patient.
Encounter	UUID	Foreign key to the Encounter where the medication was prescribed.
Code	String	Medication code from RxNorm.

Description	String	Description of the medication.
Cost	Numeric	The line-item cost of the medication.
ReasonCode	String	Diagnosis code from SNOMED-CT specifying why this medication was prescribed.
ReasonDescription	String	Description of the reason code.

The test cases for running the algorithm for the three operations are given below.

Insertion

A new record ascribing to the above format was created as below and inserted into the file.

DeStart: 2016-09-24

Stop: 2018-12-01

Patient: 123e4567-e89b-12d3-a456-426785440000

Encounter: 123e4567-e89b-12d3-a456-325655440000

Code: 573621

Description: Albuterol 0.09 MG bronchodilators.

Cost:20.43 United States Dollar (USD)

ReasonCode :195967001

Reason Description: Asthma

The record was inserted at the proper location in the skip list sorted by the *Rxcode*. The correctness of insertion was verified with a query of the *ReasonCode* from the record, which was retrieved correctly.

Updation

On the client-side, the *cost* field of the above record was modified to 20.15 USD. Updation was ensured through the use of a query of the *cost*, which returned the new value.

Deletion

This operation was performed by deleting all the records with *DeStart*as2018-06-10. A query issued for retrieval of records with the above field value did not return any record.

A fair comparison of the performance of the proposed MHT and skip list basedalgorithm and the basic pure Merkletree algorithm on the above dataset is presented for various operations.

3.5.3 Performance Metrics and Analysis

Details of the time taken for the generation of ownership proof and integrity checking are given in Table 3.2.

Table 3.2 Performance Measures-Proof Generation and Integrity Check

Block Size (No. of Records)	Merkle Tree		Merkle Tree with Skip List (Proposed)	
	Proof Generation (ms)	Integrity Check (ms)	Proof Generation (ms)	Integrity Check (ms)
16	12	16	8	11
32	23	29	17	19
64	46	59	27	31
128	105	119	86	107
256	189	217	140	180
512	458	498	398	415

A visual representation of the performance metrics isprovided in Figure 3.10. An increase in the computational time for generation of ownership proof and integrity verification with the size of the blocks is seen. It is also evident that the proposed dynamic PDP system based on both MHT and skip list exhibits superior performance compared to the Merkle Tree-based approach.

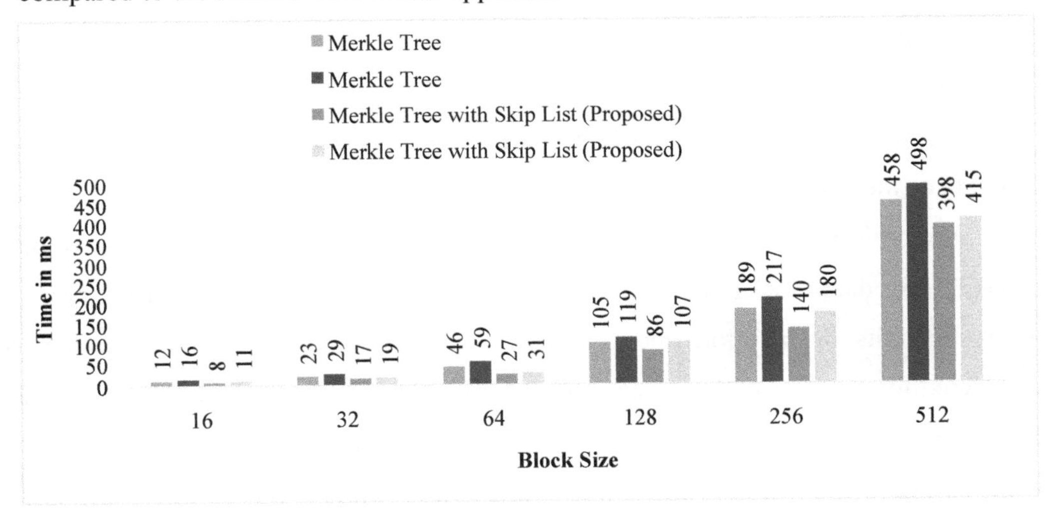

Figure 3.10 Performance Analysis- Proof Generation and Verification

The performance of the proposed system was tested with single cloud and multi-cloud environments for insertion, deletion, and updation operations for integrity check operations with the above dataset. The performance metrics given for a block size of 1024 records are shown in Figure 3.11.

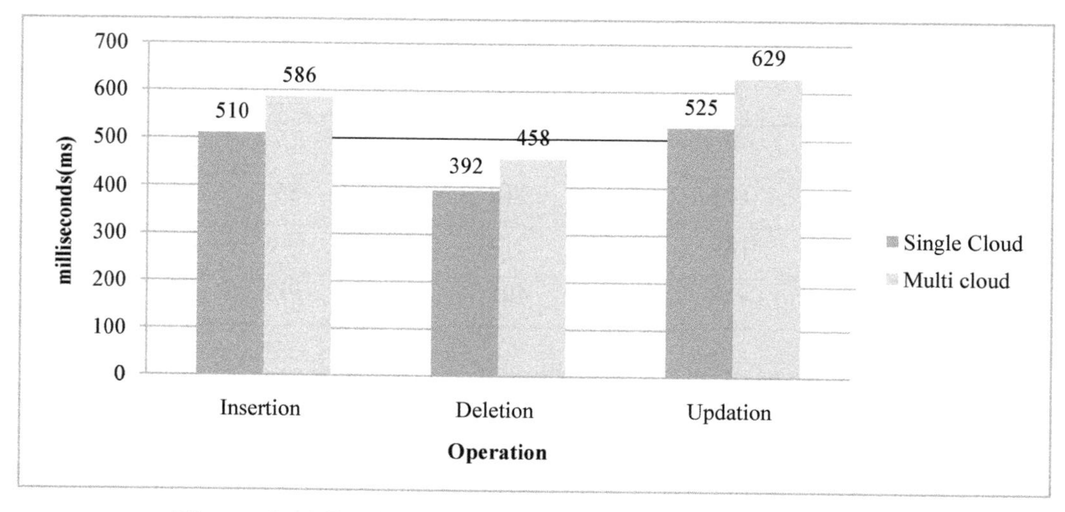

Figure 3.11 Performance Analysis –Dynamic Operations

The experimental results in the two environments show, the MHT combined with a skip list as a promising solution for multi-cloud environments. The scalability of the system wasconfirmed with the large block size chosen in the second experiment to evaluate the data dynamics of the system.

The performance of the proposed system is compared with that of similar works in Table 3.3. for data blocks of size 512. The performance metrics show that the proposed system exhibits best performance compared to the existing methods. The methods considered for comparison have been so far implemented for authentication operations in the single cloud only. Extending them for multi-cloud requires considerable modifications in the parameters to suit multi-cloud environments which does not permit exhaustive comparisons with multiple data blocks.

Table 3.3 Performance Comparison-MT with Skip List

Reference	Proof Generation(ms)	Integrity Check(ms)
Proposed Work	**398**	**415**
Li et al. [33] (2018)	409	565
Xu et al.[59] (2018)	487	515
Cho et al.[68] (2018)	589	613

3.6 SUMMARY

In this chapter, the researcher has presented a novel dynamic PDP based on MHT and skip lists. The efficacy of the proposed integrity check process is established withthe generation of proof and verification with various sized data blocks. The proposed system was tested with dynamic record insertion, deletion and modification operations with healthcare records in a simulated multi-cloud. The performance metrics resulting from the experimental worksindicate the suitability of the proposed PDP to a dynamic healthcare environment. A variety of cloud-based services can be modelled on the proposed system and scaled according to the client population.

CHAPTER 4

A DYNAMIC PROVABLE DATA POSSESSION MODEL BASED ON FRACTAL MERKLE TREE

4.1 INTRODUCTION

Merkle trees are employed in the construction of robust integrity check mechanisms in the single cloud and multi-cloud environments due to their simplicity. In the previous section, the researcher has presented an efficient MHT and Skip list- based PDP in a healthcare multi-cloud. In the conventional PDPs, integrity check was performed by comparing the proof owned by the client with that generated by the server. The presence of voluminousclient data in a multi-cloud environment increases the number of client data blocks, consequently resulting in an increase in the size of the equivalent Merkle Tree. Generally, Merkle Trees were used in the implementation of fine-grained attribute-based verification systems, for imposing access privileges on the different entities in a multi-cloudbased business model. This mechanism restricts access to sensitive data and reduces the size of data involved in hash computations.

This security model can be further strengthened by tracking and logging the access to a particular data block and the sequence of operations performed on it by various entities. This feature facilitates the quick resolution of non-repudiation attacks and faster resumption to a particular state of a system on failure. A dynamic PDP with authentication path tracking based on a Fractal Merkle Tree (FMT), which exhibits lower computational and storage complexity than the MHT based PDP is presented in this chapter. This model is suitable for resource-constrained mobile devices in multi-cloud environments for providing health rehabilitation services.

4.2 RELATED WORK

Merkle trees find wide applications in cryptographic systems. In an MHT, the integrity of a data block represented by a leaf node can be verified with the hash value assigned to the root node.The sequence of nodes on the path from the leaf node to the root forms the authentication path of a leaf. Traversal of the Merkle tree is the problem of determining the authentication paths for successive leaf nodes in an MHT. Storingevery node in the memory is impractical in multi-cloud environments due to the dynamism of enterprise applications. However, the performance of computations for determining the authentication paths is also expensive at the non-leaf nodes near to the top of the tree is also expensive. Conservation of space and computation in MHTs without conceding the security requirements is a challenging job. The concept of FMT initially proposed byJakobsson et al. [77] in 2003, has been based on the earlier works on the hash chain traversals [69,70,71].

In hash chainbased applications, the verifier is interested only in the final hash value, which is based on the initialization vector. However, in a Merkle tree, the hash codes and authentication paths between the candidate leaf node and the root node are of interest to the verifier. A multi-cloud environment and a data block may be accessed either by a single entry or multiple entities based on the access privileges. This is analogous to access to a leaf node of the MHT representation of a client file F represented as n number of data blocks.

Restricting access to a single node in an MHT, authentication protocols for broadcasting and security mechanisms to thwart wormhole attacks in wireless ad-hoc networks are implemented in [72] and [73]. This approach has also been used in secured micro-payment schemes [74,75] and authentication certificate revocation [117]. Permitting access to multiple nodes of an MHT in digital signature schemes has been exploited, PDP schemes have been described in the previous section.

The conventional MHT exhibits space and computational complexity of $O(log2N)$

and $O(logN)$ respectively for N number leaf nodes. The FMT is an improvement over MHT, which selects the nodes to be included for computation, nodes to be discarded and retained based on a fractal representation of the MHT. A detailed description of the FMT construction and related algorithms is presented in the next section.The worst-case computational complexity of FMT is 2 $logN/log\ log\ N$per verification operation and it requires a total storage capacity of around 1.5 $log2\ N/loglogN$ for storing Nhash values.

A detailed analysis of the MHT algorithm has been presented by Knecht et al. [76].The authors have presented a new algorithm for MHT traversal exploiting the space-time trade-off from [77] with the space efficiency from [78]. The authors have also investigated the impact of Pseudo-Random Number Generator (PRNG) functions on the leaf nodes. The algorithm proposed in [76] helps the achievement of space reduction by factor 2 compared to the basic algorithm proposed in [77].

In a conventional sequential hashing operation, the hash function H is iteratively applied on blocks of data of uniform size. Hence the number of data blocks determines the running time of these algorithms asymptotically. However, this function cannot provide service of the desired quality in a multi-cloud environment configured with multiple service providers, in which client data size is not static.

The concept of parallel or fast hashing on trees with a small height for resource-constrained deviceswas introduced by Kelsey [79]. Three different tree modes for parallel hashing have been reviewed by Atighehchi and Bonnecaze [80] and new modes for addressing the resource utilization problems in parallel computing environments have been proposed.

Out of three conventions used in the expression of parallel hashing, the first convention was realized with Merkle trees. In this context, a non-leaf node was obtained as a result of applying the hash function$H$ on the concatenation of the child nodes, and the leaf was taken as the result of the application of an inner hashing function on a data block bi,called as "mode 1" parallel hashing, this was realized by distributing the hashing operations among many processors and using only a single processor for sequential hashing of the concatenation of these results.

A detailed investigation of the authentication paths and the time-space complexity trade-offs in Merkle tree traversals has been undertaken by Berman et al. [118]. Integrity check mechanisms using FMTs were implemented with functions for root generation, authentication path generation, and verification. The influence of the efficiency of these mechanisms is influenced by the space and time complexity in computations in multi-cloud environments was seen.

Scheduling of jobs, which selects the next node to be taken for computation of hash values out of *n* nodes in a Merkle tree is an important process. It must be done in such a way that the authentication paths are generated faster without compromising on the latest updates in the client data. The strength of the FMT traversal lies in its ability to select the nodes for computation at each step.

FMT replaces conventional MHT in the deployment of various security mechanisms that include digital signatures and integrity verifications. FMTseq, a one- time signature scheme proposed by Naor et al. [62] based on FMT is 35 times faster than the RSA signature scheme. Inspired by this solution, several security applications based on Merkle tree traversalhave been proposed.

Recently, Berbecaru [81] implemented NetTrack, a tool for creating digital signatures for data flows and multicasts using Merkle tree traversal.Faster creation of digital evidence was demonstrated.

4.3 PROPOSED METHODOLOGY

The creation of an authentication path with an FMT traversal and algorithms for traversal is presented in this section for getting an understanding of the underlying principle of the system proposed by the researcher.

4.3.1 Authentication path creation by a fractal tree traversal

Fractal traversal of Merkle trees allows space-computation trade-offs and is structurally simple. This is illustrated in Figure 4.1 which depictsan authentication path from the leaf node to the root node, which comprises only three intermediate nodes whose values are needed for the computation of the hash value at the node. This kind of tree traversal which traverses only the nodes involved in a computation, minimizing the number of nodes to be visited, is called the fractal traversal.

The authentication path for each block of data that can be generated helps verification of the integrity of each block of data and the file as a whole. Keeping track of the modifications to the nodes in the authentication path, computations in certain nodes whose hash value has not changedcan be avoided. This traversal is integrated with the security mechanisms in cloud environments for faster verification of authentication proofs.

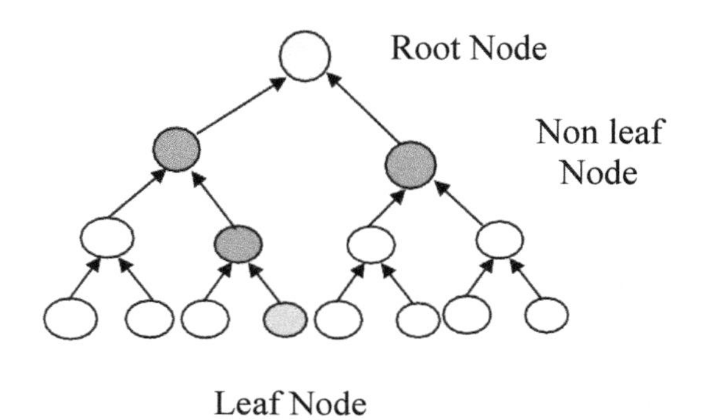

Figure 4.1 Authentication Path from Leaf Node to Root Node

4.3.2 Traversal algorithms

The integrity check mechanism is based on the evaluation of leaf values called leaf pre-images. In a cloud environment, each data block b_i of the client file F constitutes a leaf pre-image on which the one-way hash function H is applied. For non-leaf nodes, the hash values are generated by applying H on the concatenation of hash values of the left and right child nodes as given in equation (4.1).

$$H(parent)=H(H(l\_child) \,||\, H(r\_child) \quad (4.1)$$

In a Merkle tree, the hash value of the root node is public, while the hash code of each leaf and the non-leaf node is known only by the data owner. The FMT algorithm for integrity check is implemented in three phases namely key generation, authentication path generation, and verification.

The key generationalgorithm computes the hash value at a node *n*, for a tree with height *h*. It employs a function *leaf_c*which calculates the value of each leaf node *leaf*$_i$.It computes the leaf pre-image of each *leaf*$_i$in sequence initially. The algorithm is implemented with a stack that stores the hash values of each node of the tree. The hash value assigned to the root node is public. The algorithm for key generation is given in Figure 4.2.

Input: Merkle Tree M, Hash function H

Output: Stack S with hash value of each node n_i

Procedure:

1. *Create an empty stack S*

   S←NULL

// Compute the pre-image values at the leaf nodes

2. *Repeat for i← 1 to n*
   a. *pre-image*$_i$ *←leaf_c(leaf*$_i$*)*
   b. *push(S, pre-image*$_i$*)*
3. *Continue*

   // Compute the node values at the non-leaf nodes
4. *While S is not Empty*
   a. *r_child←Pop(S)*
   b. *l_child←Pop(S)*
   c. H(Parent) ← *H(H(l_child) || H(r_child)*
   d. *push(S, H(Parent))*
5. *Continue*

Figure 4.2 Algorithm for Key Generation

The authentication path generation algorithm needs a basic understanding of the FMT structure illustrated in Figure 4.3. It is seen that the Merkel hash tree *M* of height h consists of L levels, each of height j. The leaves of the hash tree are indexed from $0, 1, .. 2j - 1$ from the left towards right.

In an FMT, the height of the maximal subtree for which a node n is the root is the height of n. This height ranges from 0 for the leaves to h for the root node. A j-subtree is at level i when the height of its root is $i*j$ for any i ranging from 1, 2, ..., L. For each level i there exist $2h-i*j$ such subtrees. A sequence of j-subtrees {$Tree_i$}, i=1...L is a stacked series if for all $i< L$ the root of $Tree_i$is a leaf of $Tree_{i+1}$.

In the above representation, $Exist_i$refers to a series of existing subtrees whose authentication path is stacked. There is a set of desired subtrees apart from these subtrees. For each existing tree $Exist_i$with index a, there exists a desired subtree $Desire_i$of index $a+1$. For any arbitrary node n in a tree M, a *pebble* is placed on a node*n*due to the storage of its hash code $H(n)$ is stored in the stack S.

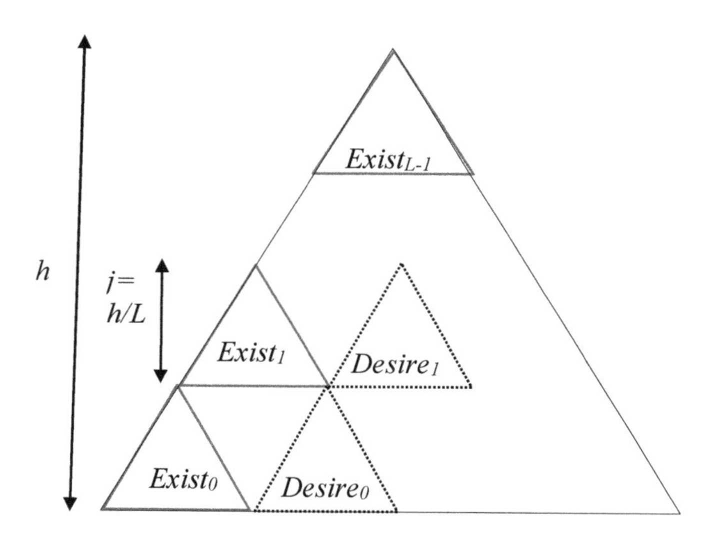

Figure 4.3 Fractal MerkleHash Tree

When a subtree $Exist_i$ is used in the previous computation of an authentication map, it said to *die*. For the next computation, all its nodes but the root of $Desire_i$must be assigned the hash value. The verification process involves a simple comparison of hash values computed at the client with the value assigned to the root node. They are always computed before the computation of the hash node of the parent at level $i+1$. The algorithm for authentication path generation is given in Figure 4.4.

Input: Merkle Tree M, Stack S with hash value of each node n_i

Output: Authentication path for each node n_i

Procedure:

1. *Set leaf to 0*
   a. *leaf ← 0*
2. *Output Authentication Path for leaf number leaf*
   a. *Print leaf.path*
3. *Repeat for i ←1 to L*
   a. *Construct the $Subtree_i$ for each i for which $Exist_i$ is used in the previous computation*
   b. *Remove Pebbles in $Exist_i$*
   c. *Rename tree $Desire_i$ as $Exist_i$*
   d. *Create new empty tree $Desire_i$*
4. *Grow subtrees $Desire_i$ for each i ←1 to j*
5. *leaf←leaf+1*
6. *Loop to step 2 until leaf<=2h*

Figure 4.4 Algorithm for Authentication Path Generation

4.4 ARCHITECTURE OF PROPOSED METHODOLOGY

This section presents the architecture of the proposed FMT based PDP and integrity check process for dynamic client operations.

4.4.1 Architecture of FMT based PDP

The schematic of the proposed PDP based on FMT is shown in Figure 4.5. This PDP model was implemented with the algorithms in Figures4.2 and 4.4 and the following auxiliary functions.

KeyGen(PRNG) $\rightarrow \{p_k, s_k\}$

This function generates a pair of keys comprising the public key p_k and the private key s_k.

TagBlock(F) $\rightarrow \{b_1, b_2 \ldots b_{n,m}\}$

This function is run by the client to create block sequences from F, generate metadata of F and assign tags to the blocks.

The client represents the file F, as a set of n blocks $\{b_1, b_2 \ldots b_n\}$ and shares with the server,which is stored in the cloud. The client maintains $E_{Sk}(F)$, an encrypted copy of F, generated by encrypting F with the secret key S_k. The key values are converted into tags applying the hash function H. The tag values are organized in the form of an FMT by the client and shared with the server. The integrity check is performed by generating the authentication path and verifying the node value at the root using the traversal algorithm.

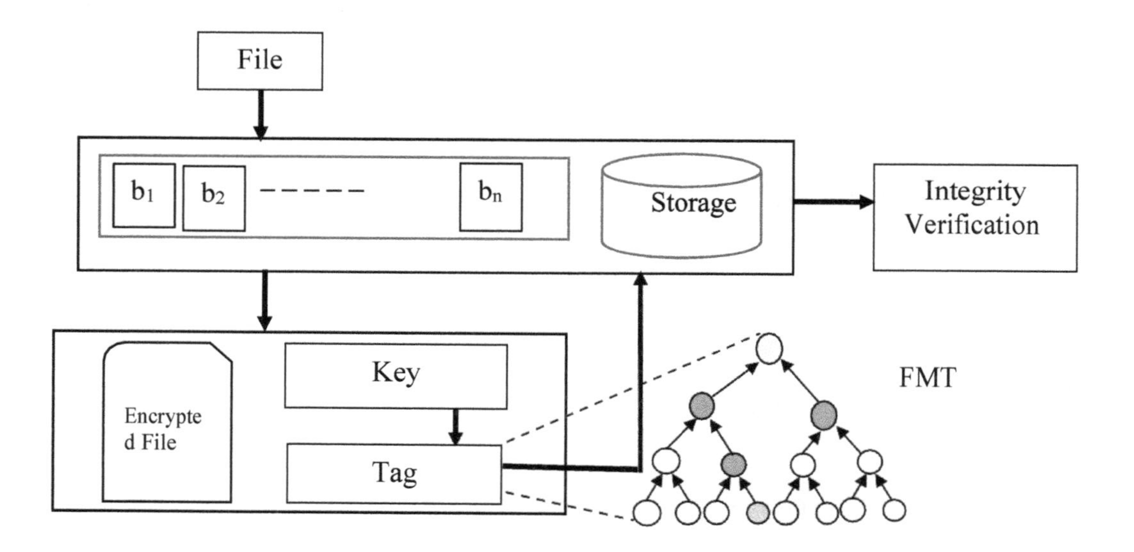

Figure 4.5 FMT based Dynamic PDP

4.4.2 Integrity verification process

Modifications to the contents of any of the data blocks $b_i$arereplicated on the respective key k_i and tag t_i and these values are updated by the client in the FMT. The client sends the integrity check request to the server and gets the authentication path of the leaf node along with the leaf pre-images. The hash value associated with the root node is compared with that of the FMT in the client. A match indicates the client data is not tampered with and is dynamically updated in the server. If there is a difference, the authentication path is traversed for localizing the error. A detailed description of the integrity verification processes for the insertion, deletion and updation operations is provided in this section.

Insertion

On insertion of a new block b_{n+1}, the key k_{n+1} and the tag $t_{n+1}$are generated bythe client and sent to the server. A new node $n+1$ is inserted into the FMT. On a verification operation for a leaf node $leaf_i$, it is checked for a fall in the new node on its authentication path. If so, $Exist_i$is recomputed and $H(n+1)$ is pushed into the stack. Otherwise, computations are carried out with $Desire_i$.A query is submitted by the client for retrieval of data from the new data block b_{n+1}, and for ensuring the correctness of the insertion operation.

Deletion

On deletion of an existing block b_i, the client deletes the node from the tree M, reorganizes the tree andrecomputes the hash values of the nodes. The $Exist_i$and $Desire_i$subtrees of each node i are modified. On a verification operation for a leaf node $leaf_i$, it is checked for modification of the $Exist_i$and $Desire_i$subtrees. If so, computations are performed with $Exist_i$. The client verifies the correctness of the operation with a query to retrieve data from the non-existent node.

Updation

On modifying the content of a data block b_i, the client recomputes the hash values and substitutes the old hash code with the new value in the stack S. The authentication paths on which the modified node of $b_i$is identified and the corresponding *Exist*and *Desire*subtrees are modified. On a verification operation for a leaf node $leaf_i$, it is checked formodification of$Exist_i$and $Desire_i$subtrees. If so,computations are performed with $Exist_i$. The client verifies the correctness of the operation with a query to retrieve data from the modified node. Otherwise, computations are carried out with $Desire_i$. Finally, the client places a request to the server for retrieval of the modified content from the block b_i.

4.5 EXPERIMENTAL RESULTS AND DISCUSSIONS

4.5.1 Experimental setup

The proposed system was implemented to enable a fair comparison and tested in the multi-cloud environment similar to the MHT and Skip list based PDP, discussed in Chapter 3. Performance metrics were evaluated. The multi-cloud environment was configured with the Cloud Simulator, Google Drive, Dropbox and Cloud Me. The protocol for data integrity check was implemented with algorithms for the generation of keys and authentication path generation in Java with Eclipse as the front end. The proposed system was implemented and tested in two different environments.

In the first, the time to search for a set of data blocks $\{b_i\}$from the n nodes in an MHT and FMT was evaluated. In the second, the proof generation and integrity verification times were computed and compared with MHT and skip list-based PDP.

Similar to the previous experiments, the size of the public and private keys is fixed as 160 bits in this experiment as well.

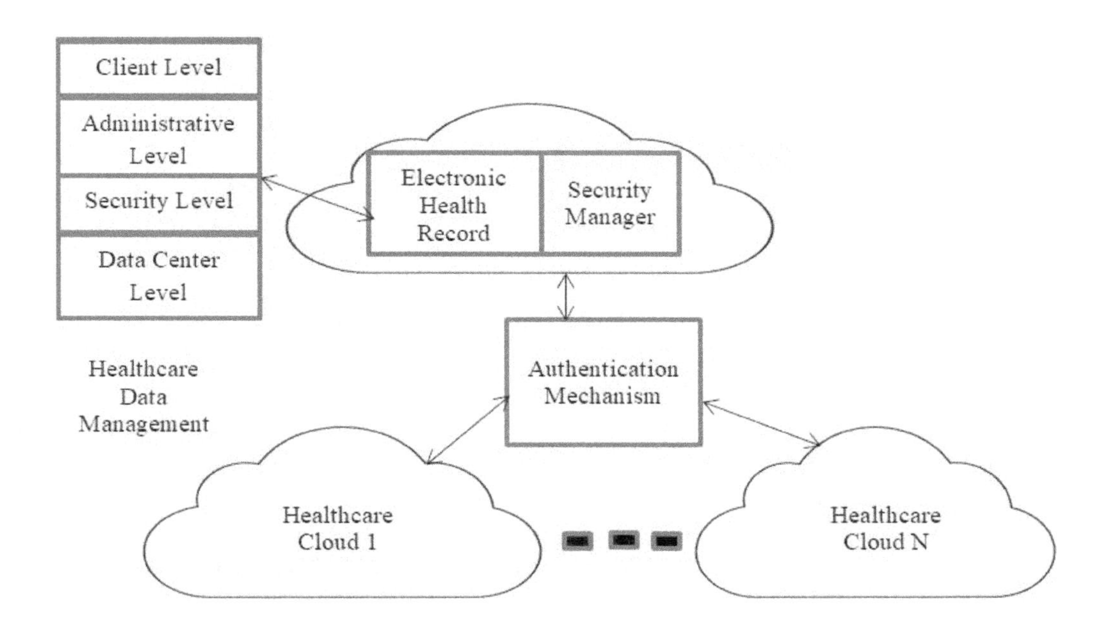

Figure 4.6 Multi Cloud Environment for FMT based Dynamic PDP

4.5.2 Test cases and results

The first set of experiments was conducted with a client file *F* with 512 records containing the attributes *DeStart, Stop, Patient, Encounter, Code, Description, Cost, ReasonCode, Reason Description* which is described in Table 3.1. The time taken for search, for the number of searches into this dataset are graphically represented in Figure 4.7 Search times are seen as lower for FMT which linearly aligns with that of MHT with respect to the number of searches.

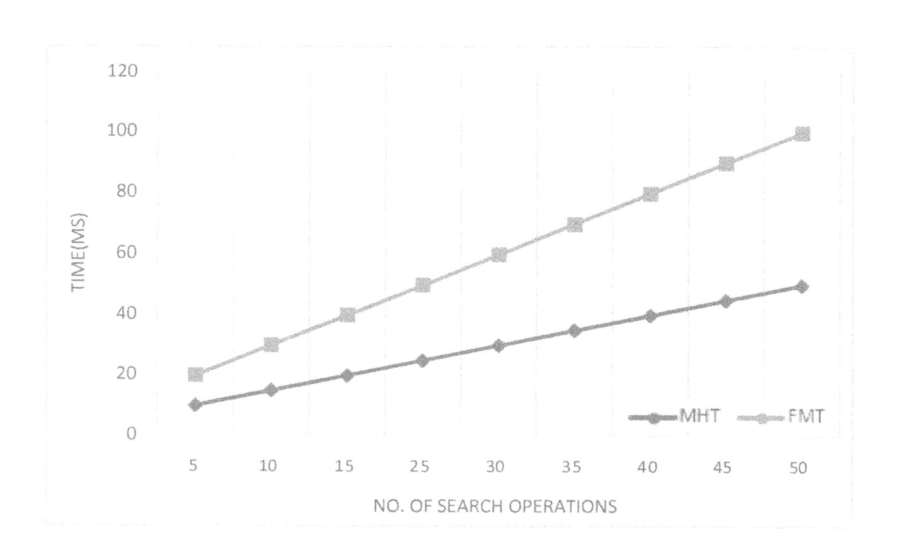

Figure 4.7 Search Times –MHT and FMT

The test cases taken up for the second set of experiments werelisted as below.

Insertion

The following record was created inserted into the file.

DeStart: 2016-09-24

Stop: 2018-12-10

Patient: 123e4567-e89b-12d3-a456-426785440000

Encounter: 123e4567-e89b-12d3-a456-325655440000

Code: 573621

Description: Albuterol 0.09 MG bronchodilators

Cost:20.43 USD

ReasonCode :195967001

Reason Description: Asthma

The corresponding node was inserted at the proper position in the tree, based on which the $Exist_i$and $Desire_i$subtrees were modified. The correctness of insertion was verified with a query of the *Encounter* field from the record, which was retrieved correctly.

Updation

At the client-side, the *cost* field of the above record was modified to 20.15 USD. Updation was ensured throughthe issue of a query relating to the *cost*, which returned the new value.

Deletion

This operation was performed by deleting all the records with *DeStart as 2018-06-10.*A query issued for retrieval of records with the above field value did not return any record.

The performance of the proposed algorithm was compared with the pure Merkle-tree algorithm on the above dataset. The performance metrics for the second set of experiments are given in Table 4.1.

Table 4.1 Performance Measures-Proof Generation and Integrity Check

Block Size (No. of Records)	Merkle Tree with Skip List		Fractal Merkle Tree (Proposed)	
	Proof Generation (ms)	Integrity Check (ms)	Proof Generation (ms)	Integrity Check (ms)
16	8	11	5	7
32	17	19	13	15
64	27	31	23	26
128	86	107	56	84
256	140	180	120	152
512	398	415	350	380

Figure 4.8. is a visual representation of the performance metrics. It is clear that the computational times for ownership proof generation and integrity verification are lower for FMT based PDP than the MHT and skip list based PDP.

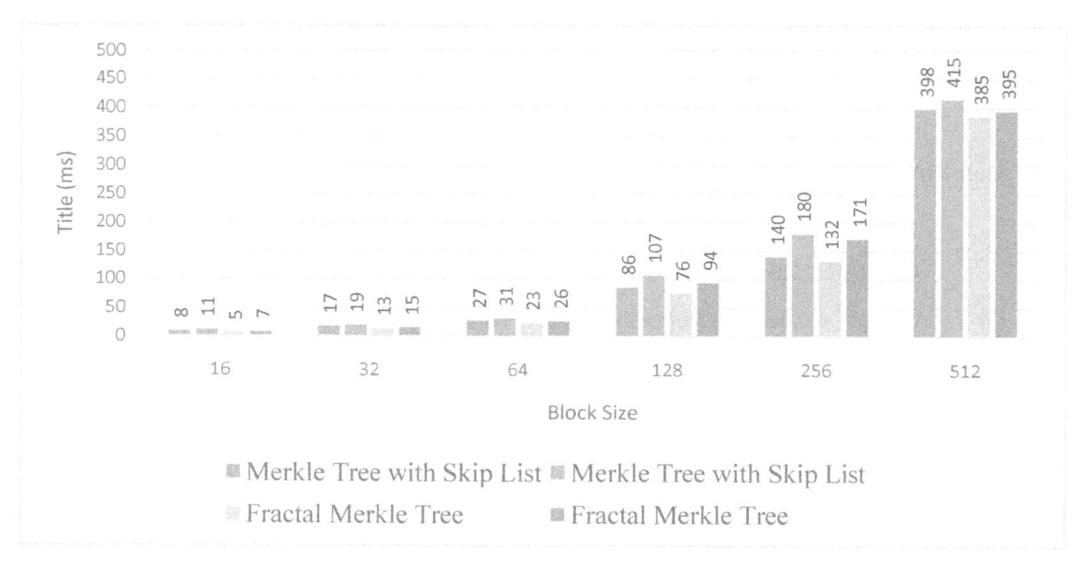

Figure 4.8 Performance Analysis-Proof Generation and Integrity check Times

The superiority of the FMT based PDP to the MHT and skip list-based PDP with respect to search time, proof generation and verification have been demonstrated.

4.5.3 Space and Computational complexity analysis

This section presents a detailed analysis of space and time complexities based on [77].The mathematical notations for complexity evaluation given in Table 4.2. relate to a tree with N nodes.

Table 4.2 Space and Computational Complexity

Method	Space Complexity	Computational Complexity
MHT+Skip List	*log2N*	*logN*
FMT	$1.5\ log^2\ N/loglogN$	*2 logN/loglogN*

The researcher has assumed a client file *F* with 2^{20} records and six block sizeseach of 16, 32, 64, 128, 256 and 512 records. The number of data blocks is equivalent to the number of nodes *N*of the tree with variationswith respect to the block size. A comparison of the space and computational complexity of the MHT and skip list based PDP and the FMT based PDP for different block sizesare provided in Table 4.3

Table 4.3 Space and Time Complexity Metrics

Record Size	No. of Blocks	Merkle Tree with Skip List		Fractal Merkle Tree (Proposed)	
		Space Complexity	Computational Complexity	Space Complexity	Computational Complexity
16	65536	17	16	12.00	2.41
32	32768	16	15	11.52	2.31
64	16384	15	14	11.03	2.21
128	8192	14	13	10.54	2.12
256	4096	13	12	10.04	2.02
512	2048	12	11	9.54	1.91

The FMT based system is seen as having a lower space and computational complexities than the MHT and a skip list based PDP for all block sizes. Reduction in the space and computational complexities by a factor of 1.3 and 6 respectively, in the FMT, based PDP was also seen. Low computational complexity is attributed to the representation of *Exist* and *Desire* subtrees, which are selectively used in the computation. The researcher performed the above computations in log_2scale with the file and block size chosen in powers of 2.

Another interesting observation from the result relates tothe feature of the complexities,as proportional to the number of blocks rather than the block sizes. As the number of blocks is equivalent to the number of nodes *N*, the complexity is seen as low in the Merkle trees when their nodes are small in number. Figure 4.9. is a graphical representation of the space and computational complexities for a visual interpretation.

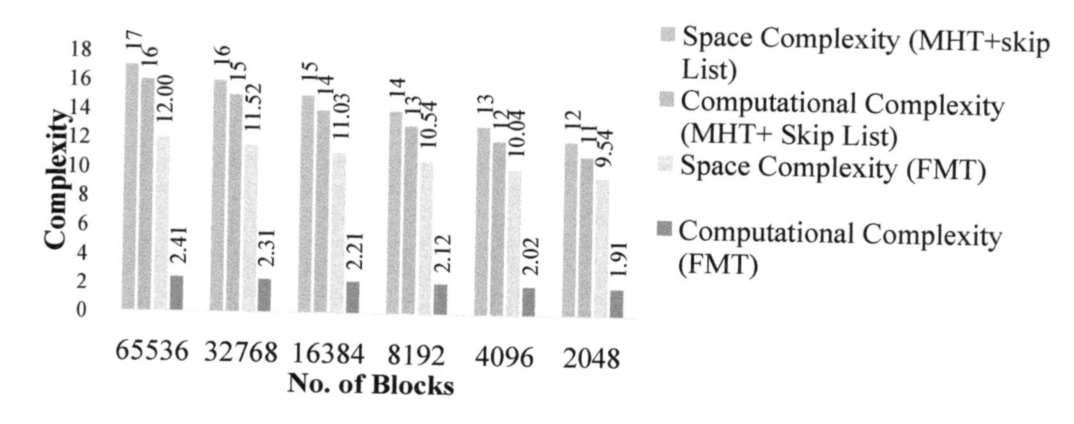

Figure 4.9Space and Computational Complexity Analysis

The successful application of this approach depends upon the complexities involved in the implementation of the proposed system. A comparison of the space and time complexities for implementation of the combined MHT and FMT based integrity verification is given in Table 4.4. It is seen that the complexities are low for the proposed system compared to the other verification systems. Out of the systems taken for comparison only [77] implements the FMT exclusively for integrity verification. From this it is understood that combination of MHT and FMT improves the performance of the integrity verification process.

Table 4.4 Performance Comparison-MHT with FMT

Reference	Space Complexity	Computational Complexity
Proposed Work	9.54	1.91
Jakobsson et al. [77] (2003)	9.86	2.76
Li et al. [33] (2018)	10.45	3.11
Xu et al.[59] (2018)	13.01	2.19
Cho et al.[68] (2018)	14.09	4.09

4.6 SUMMARY

In this chapter, a novel dynamic PDP based FMT for a multi-cloud environment is presented and its efficacywas testified by experiments. The proposed PDP model was tested with dynamic record insertion, deletion and modification operations on healthcare records with well-designed test cases in a simulated multi-cloud. The authentication paths generated in the proposed system were seen as highly significant in the resolution of server and client-side repudiation attacks due to the publicly available hash code of the root of the tree. TheFMT did simplification of thelocalization of tampering by traversal of the authentication paths. The experimental results showed the feature of the excellent performance of proposed FMT based PDP with proof generation and integrity verification, highly desirable in a security mechanism. Beyond that, the lower space and computational complexities were seen indicative of its appropriateness, in designing prospective solutions in the dynamic healthcare environment, for speedy provision of clinical services. Ascribing to its simplicity, this model can be integrated with any heterogeneous cloud infrastructure with compelling QoS requirements.

CHAPTER 5

POSITION AWARE MERKLE TREE BASED DYNAMIC DATA INTEGRITY VERIFICATION MECHANISM FOR CLOUD-BASED REHABILITATION SERVICES

5.1 INTRODUCTION

The subject matter of the last two chapters was the implementation of PDPs based on MHT and FHT and then demonstrated dynamic ability in integrity verification, in challenging and highly constrained medical cloud environments. In recent years, cloud-based utility service providers have seen a tremendous progressionin the client population. Simultaneously, the complexity in the design of the service models has also increased due to the rapid mobility of the clients, diversity of the client devices, resource constraints with mobile devices, etc. Service providers devise solutions centred on these dynamic factors for assuring the best QoS. In continuation ofthe researcher's investigations on PDPs for medical clouds, the research was carried forward to an exigent domain of rehabilitation services.

Of late, healthcare systems have undergone a major transformation by hosting their services on the cloud, enabling the delivery of services to remote destinations. Distributed environments are configured to house Health Information Systems (HIS) for providing expert care on the fly in emergencies. Rapid delivery of services requires immediate access to the historical and real-time patient data from the distributed cloud storage devices. This dynamic requirement of data is also coupled with strong security and privacy concerns.

Stringent legislative guidelines allow a patient the facility of providing a definition of the security constraints on personal and clinical data. Recent security mechanisms have been modelled on this requirement, enabling the patient to exercise controls on data with simple user interfaces as in a system proposed by Sicuranza et al. [119]. The dearth of rehabilitation service providers has led to the provision of these services over the cloud. The motivation of subjects is a vital component of rehabilitation services. Most recently, López-Jaquero et al. [120] have proposed aninfluence awareness model and conceptualized on motivation theories to simplify this process.

Despite the dynamism and simplicity requirements of cloud-based rehabilitation services, there is an overwhelming need for security mechanisms. A subset of client data in the medical cloud is subjected to frequent access and modifications by caregivers. Ensuring the accuracy of data is very crucial in the cloud environment, for assurance of proper delivery of care. Impeccable authentication and integrity verification mechanisms are matters of prime concern in rehabilitation services for preventingthe breach of security and privacy. Compromises in these mechanisms result in the abuse of data, affecting the reputation of the care provider and privacy of the subject.

The focus of this chapter, is on the implementation of a PDP suitable for rehabilitation services, addressing integrity verification and QoS. The proposed system has been realized as a publicly verifiable system for integrity protection, supporting dynamic updates in real-time healthcare data, with optimal storage, time and computational complexities. Publicly verifiable computation is a crucial requirement in the medical cloud when computations out-sourced by weak clients. Gennaro et al. [121] have introduced a publicly verifiable scheme and proved its ability to provide privacy of data and reliability of services.

Though authentication is not explicitly addressed, this feature has also been realized implicitly in the proposed system because of the underlying data structure. The proposed system has been built on the PMT [82], in which each node is capable of determining its relative position to other nodes in the tree from the 3-tuple representation. Integrity verification was performed at each node from the hash codes of the root nodes of the subtrees.

In the following sections,elaborate reviews of the research work related to this context, a description of the underlying methodology, architecture of the proposed system, experimental results and interpretations are all presented.

5.2 RELATED WORK

The PMT based publicly verifiable integrity verification system proposed by Mao et al. [83] in 2017 is the first of its kind in the cloud environment. This system envisages data integrity verification as an indispensable security mechanism in thecloud, in the purview of clients outsourcing the data to remote service providers. It employs the challenge-response model for the performance of integrity verifications.

In continuation of the above, the same authors have proposed an integrity check mechanism for the verification of heterogeneous sensor data in a multi-cloud environment. It employs a parallel checking mechanism with distributed storage devices for integrity checks.

Auditing the behaviour of users is very vital for the prevention of unauthorized data access and integrity verification in the cloud. Digital forensic applications employ statistical models and cryptographic systems for the investigation of the integrity of data in multi-cloud environments. An MHT based public user log auditing mechanism proposed by Tian et al. [85] has demonstrated the performance of secure auditing with low communication and computation overheads.

In continuance with the above, the same authors have also recently proposed a block-basedlogging approach employing a binary auditing tree for the enforcement of tamper resistance in log files, prevention of non-repudiation of user actions and verification of specific blocks of log files. Further, this approach also facilities localization of errors during dynamic client operations.

Since client data storedis in the form of records in the cloud environment, record integrity check schemes are also introduced for verification of static and dynamic records. There exist multiple replicas of client data in distributed storage devices for proof of ownership. Modification of client data requires perfect reflection in all the copies to ensure data integrity. Levitin et al. [86] have addressed the vulnerability of Virtual Machines (VM) to co-residence attacks and proposed a probabilistic model for the capture of user behaviour. Optimization problems were formulated based on the behaviour of genuine users and attackers and solutions were proposed for defeating side-channel attacks, data theft, and tampering.

Cloud environments implemented with weak security mechanisms are victims of side-channel attacks. Koo et al. [67] have proposed an MHT based authentication scheme in which, the authentication proof is encrypted for the defeat of guessing attacks by the adversary. It is impractical for an attacker to recover the proof, extract the root values of subtrees and launch attacks on client data in a dynamic cloud environment. The verification scheme of Cho et al. [68], based on MHT has demonstrated better reliability than log-based schemes in the verification of personal data residing at multiple storage devices in the cloud.

A Verifiable Data Model (VDM) proposed by Eltayesh et al. [122],following the Bayesian security game approach, facilitates the integrity verification of data distributed across multiple databases. It also demonstrates the best QoS characteristics in cloud environments with multiple followers of the same data.

A TPA scheme based on Message Authentication Code (MAC) proposed by Wan et al. [123], with the reduced computational cost is ideal for resource-constrained devices. Such systems can also be constructed with MHTs exploiting the hash codes at each node. There are many security issues in the cloud environment that scale up in medical clouds due to the rigidity in data access. It is essential to select appropriate conventional methodologies and design new solutions based on the underlying cloud infrastructure, client expectations, and complexities involved in the deployment. An investigation of traditional and recent security solutions by Kiraz [124] strongly advocates the need for this assessment.

Attacks on outsourced computations from adversaries in cloud environmentsare possible. The protection of computations from interventions by attackers is vital for establishing the reliability and accuracy of solutions.A public auditing scheme proposed by Li et al. [125] helps the prevention of attacks on computations, in spite of the Key Generation Centre (KGC) being compromised.

Cryptographic systems are centred around modular arithmetic operations, due to their intrinsic computational complexity. Outsourcing modular exponentiation computations to a public key cryptosystem were successfully demonstrated by Hohenberger and Lysyanskaya [126]. Xiang and Tang [127] have proposed two schemes with similar features that enable the client to perform computations with variable numeric bases and perform modular exponentiations simultaneously with the server.

Irrespective of the prevalence of security mechanisms, application-specific security systems are deployed by service providers based on the requirements of clients. Premkamal et al. [128] have proposed a cryptographic system for fine-grained data access called Ciphertext-Policy Attribute-Based Encryption (CP-ABE), for protection of client data at the attribute level, protection of computation and integrity verification. In addition, it limits the number of users and restricts the frequency of data access with a well-defined access control policy.

In publicly verifiable integrity verification, auditing is entrusted to the TPAs forassuranceof the integrity of data in storage devices and retrieval of the updated data block, employing Proof of Retrievability (PoR) protocol. Wang et al. [129] have proposed a model based on the homomorphic signature and MHT for integrity verification with data insertion, deletion, and modification.

Since the PMT based integrity verification is in its infancy, the above mechanisms have not yet been implemented with the PMT. However, the ability of these mechanisms to do effective realization with the PMT, which is structurally similar to the MHT but faster in retrieval compared to MHT and its variants is also clearly seen.

Complexities in the delivery of healthcare services over the cloud have been documented by researchers. New models integrating heterogeneous healthcare frameworks have been proposed. A hybrid model comprising cloud infrastructure and the Internet of Things (IoT) proposed by Elhoseny et al. [90], optimizes the selection of VMs in the cloud-IoT integral environment to help the handling of large volumes of data for healthcare applications.

Two significant works on cloud-based services for the rehabilitation of stroke patients have been presented by Bai et al. [91,92]. Perceiving the difficulty in the rehabilitation of the upper limb, the authors have proposed a cost-effective home- based rehabilitation system, creating training and assessment scenes accessible over the cloud. The results of the assessment model and clinical trials were seen as promising,leading to the authors' intention towards extending the model to the evaluation of the motor functions of the palms and fingers.

Based on the analysis of the security requirements for cloud-based applications, mathematical foundations of security mechanisms, the significance of rehabilitation services and the challenges in devising security solutions for the medical cloud, the researcher employed PMT for the deployment of the proposed system.

5.3 PROPOSED METHODOLOGY

This section presents the structure of the PMT and the integrity verification algorithm to enable appreciation of the functionalities of this data structure and understanding of the architecture of the proposed system.

5.3.1 Structure of the PMT

The capacity of the MT to counter attacks on the integrity of data with many security mechanisms in dynamic cloud environmentshas been demonstrated. The PMT, an improved version of the basic MHT proposed by Mao et al. [83], adds a new dimension to the cryptographic systems. Each node in a PMT keeps track of its position relative to the root node. An arbitrary node *n* maintains its location with a 3-

tuple $\{n.U, n.S, n.W\}$, where $n.U$ is the position of $n$relativeto its root node. $n.S$ is the number of leaf nodes of n and $n.W$ is the cost of n. The path for integrity verification is generated in a PMT from the root of the tree directly without retrieving tree structure completely.The structure of the PMT is shown in Figure 5.1.

Nodes in the layers werelabelled in sequence from left to right in all the layers and $n.U$and $n.S$values were computed as follows.

$$n.U = \begin{cases} 0, if\ n \in left\_subtree \\ 1, if\ n \in rig?t\_subtree \\ null, if\ n\ is\ root \end{cases}$$

$$n.S = \begin{cases} n\_l.S + n\_r.S, if\ n\ is\ a\ nonleaf\ node \\ 1, if\ n\ is\ a\ leaf\ node \end{cases}$$

The hash value assigned to each leaf node is the MAC for the data block represented by that node. The hash codes of the non-leaf nodes authenticated the respective child nodes collectively, i.e. the client data blocks represented by them. With each node in a PMT having knowledge of its relative position, data blocks in a tree were accessed with ease, following the positioning scheme. Similarly, proofs of ownership were generated by ensuring the data block residing at a particular position.

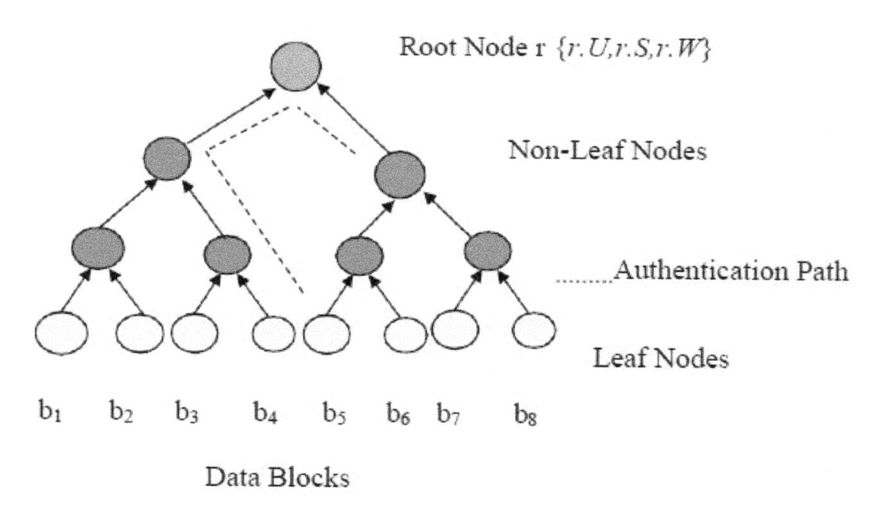

Figure 5.1 Structure of a PMT

5.3.2 PMT based Integrity Verification algorithm

The process of integrity verification with PMT is generally initiated by the client. The client computes a challenge c_i, for adata block b_i and generates the authentication proof p_i and forwards the tuple $\{p_i, c_i, i\}$ to the server. The node corresponding to the data block $b_i$is located by the server, traversing the PMT from the root node. Following the location of the candidate node n_i, the authentication proof p_i'' is generated by applying the hash function H on the concatenation of c_i and the value of the node $n_i.W$. This proof p_i'' is forwarded by the server to the client and compared with p_i for data integrity verification. The algorithm for PMT based integrity verification is given in Figure 5.2.

Input: Client data D, number of challenges k, challenges $\{c_i, i=1..k,\}$
Hash Function H

Output: ownership proofs p_i, p_i'', *verification code v*

Procedure:

1. *Divide the D into a sequence of n data blocks* $\{bi, i=1..n\}$
2. *Construct the Position Aware Merkle Tree P*
3. *Repeat for* $i \leftarrow 1$ *to k*
   a. *Compute challenge* c_i *at client C*
   b. *Compute the proof* p_i *at C*
      i. $p_i \leftarrow H(c_i || b_i)$
   c. *Transfer* $\{p_i, c_i, i\}$ *to the server S*
   d. *Locate the node* n_i*in P*
   e. *Compute the proof* p_i'' *at S*
      i. $p_i'' \leftarrow H(c_i || n_i.W)$
   f. *Transmit* p_i'' *to C*
   g. *Compare* p_i *and* p_i''.
      If $p_i = p_i''$ *then* $v \leftarrow$ *„data is not tampered"*
      Else $v \leftarrow$ *„data is tampered"*

ig ur e 5.2 Al go rit h m fo r P M T ba se d Integrity Verification

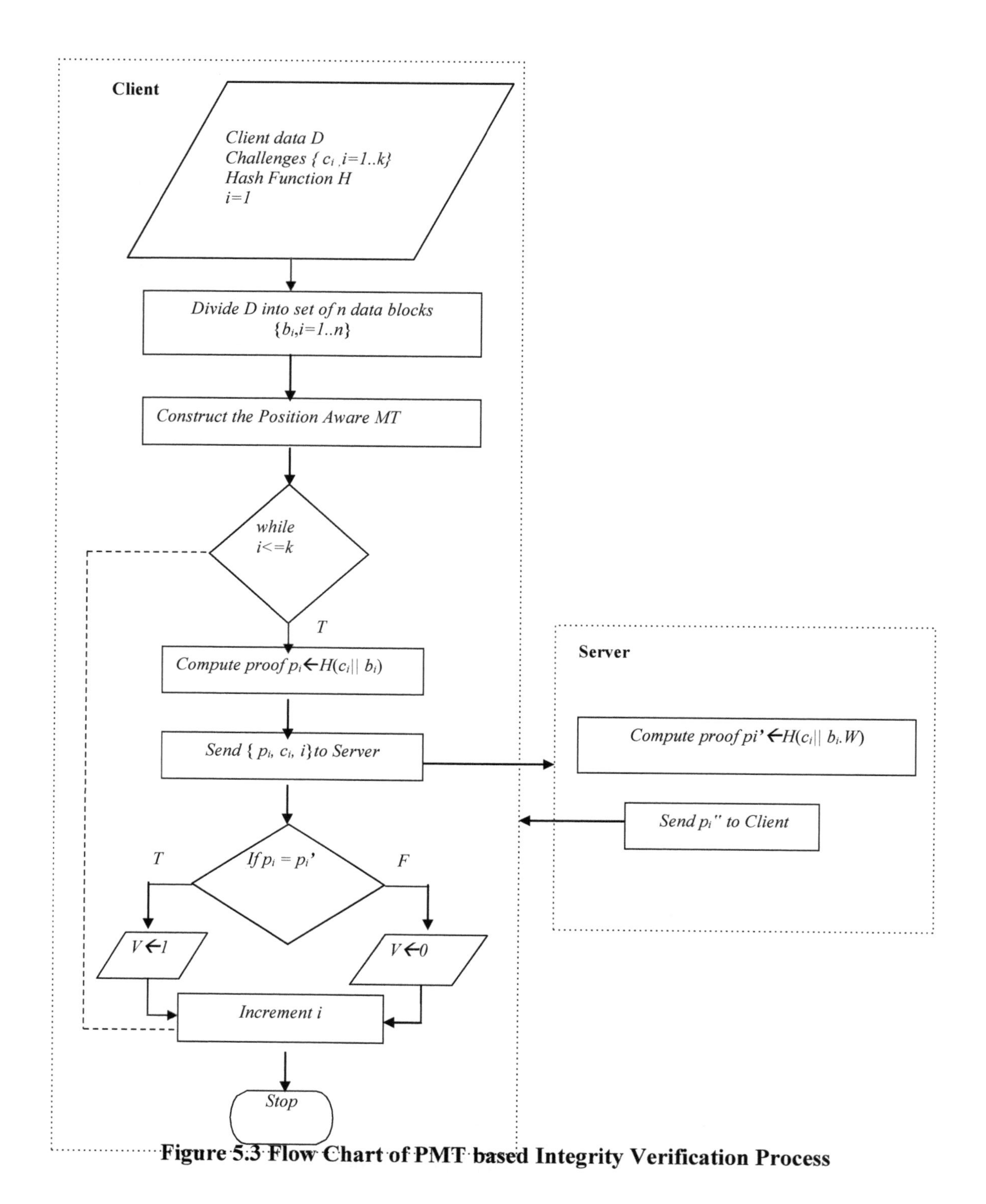

Figure 5.3 Flow Chart of PMT based Integrity Verification Process

Figure 5.3 shows theflowchart depicting the PMT based integrity verification process, clearly depicting the client-server data flows, computations performed at both the entities and the comparison at the client. The verification code *V* is binary and it is assigned „ *1"* when the data is intact and assigned „ *0"* when the data has tampered.

5.4 ARCHITECTURE OF PROPOSED METHODOLOGY

This section presents the architecture of the PMT based integrity verification system, the processes for ownership verification and integrity verification for insertion, deletion and updation operations on the client data.

5.4.1 The architecture of the PMT Based Integrity Verification System

The schematic of the PMT based integrity verification system based on the algorithm in Figure 5.2 is shown in Figure 5.4.

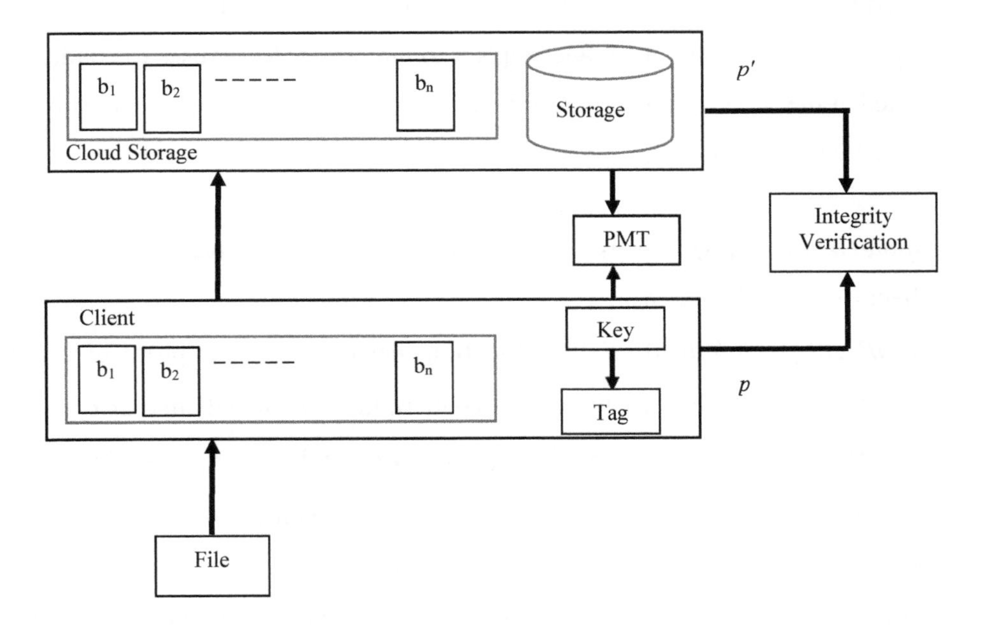

Figure 5.4 Architecture of PMT based Integrity Verification System

The PMT based integrity verification system is implemented with the protocol comprising three phases described below.

Phase I (*Initialize*): It is a set of client-side methods for initialization of system variables using the functions as below.

1. ***KeyGn(k)*** function generates a public and private key pair {*uk, tk*} from *k*, the input security parameter.
2. ***TagGen(tk,uk, M)*** $\rightarrow$ $\boldsymbol{\theta}$, the function maps the client-side metadata *M* into the tag θusing the key pair {*uk, tk*}.

The client transfers *M*along with θ to the server which is then stored in a remote cloud storage device. The client saves *M* personally or signs *M* to be stored by the server.

Phase II *(Dispute-prov)*: This phase is concerned with the generation and verification of integrity proof employing the *Dispute-prov*method. The client creates the challenge corresponding to the data block and sends it to the server. Responses to challenges are computed at the server, transferred to the client and verified by the client. This process is realized with the following functions.

1. ***DisputeGen(d)***$\rightarrow$ ***disp*** is a mapping function that maps a private parameter *d* from the client to the challenge *disp.*
2. ***ProofGen(gs, M,θ,disp)***$\rightarrow$***U*** is a function that generates the proof of ownership *U*from the client's public variable *gs*, metadata*M*, tag θ, and challenge *disp*.
3. ***ProofVerify(uk,disp,M,U)***$\rightarrow$**{"recognize","refuse"}** is a mapping function thatgenerates the binary responses signifying the correctness of the proof from the public key *uk*, challenge *disp*, metadata*M* and the proof *U.*
4. ***Confirm (root,*** x_i**)** $\rightarrow$ **{*"accept", "refuse"*}**isa function that computes the hash values in the authentication path between the root node and any leaf node $x_i$and verifies the correctness of the hash value at the root.

Phase III (*Renew*): This phase is concerned with the regeneration of authentication proof based on the dynamic operations of multiple clients in the distributed cloud. It is accomplished with the following functions.

1. ***ExecuteRenew(uk, M, θ, renew)*** → ***{M, θ, Urenew}*** is a function thatgenerates a proof *Urenew*for the modifiedclient data on a request initiated by the client. This function also recomputes the metadata *M* and the tag *θ*.
2. ***RenewAuthenticate(uk, restore, M, Urenew)*** → ***{"recognize", "refuse"}*** is a binary mapping function forthe verification of the new proof created whenever the client data is modified. This function takes the public key *uk*, *restore*flag, metadata*M* and the modified proof *Urenew*as input and generates the binary response {*"recognize"*, *"refuse"*}to enableverification of theauthentication proof for the data content updated by the client.

In this phase, the PMT is traversed and modified to reflect the changes arising as a result of the client operations. The hash values of the nodes are modified at the leaf nodes and recomputed at the non-leaf nodes and the root of the tree. Similarly, the value of the tuple {*n.U, n.S, n.W*} is modifiedfor each node *n*.

5.4.2 Verification of Ownership

The organization of storage devices in a cloud environment can be mapped to a PMT and the unambiguousproof of ownership of data block $b_i$by a remote device $x_i$can be established. Let *root* = {*root.U, root.S, root.W*} be the 3-tuple representation of the root node of the PMT and $b=\{b_i,\ i=1,2,..n\}$ be the sequence of nodes in the authentication path from any data block b_i to *root,* the root node of the tree.The function *confirm (root,* b_i*)*is invoked by the client for the verification ofthe correctness of the hash value at the root node for proof of ownership. The function "*confirm*" returns "*accept*" if *root.W* matches with that of the client or "*refuse*" otherwise. On mismatch, PMT can be traversed along the authentication path for the location of the node contributing to the error.

5.4.3 Integrity verification for Dynamic Operations

The data outsourced by the clients are manipulated with the insertion, deletion or updation operations. In a multi-cloud environment with numerous clients, the result of these operations isreflected in the replicas of the data maintained in multiple storage devices. Authentication under such a dynamic environment is simplified using the PMT as for any node *n,*with the nodes along its authentication path getting updated. The integrity check procedure under dynamic client operations must be well- defined to ensure data integrity. The verification processes for insertion, deletion, and modification operations are described below.

Data Updation

When a client intends to alter the nth data block b_n, it sends a query "*restore* = *An*, x_n, *m*" to the server, where *An* is the root node and *m* is the metadata. In response to this, the server updates the hash value at node *An* and the subtrees along the path to x_n.The server computes(¬*An 1.U, 1, h* (¬*An 1.Uadjust* ()), the new hash value at *An* to generate a new PMT named *T*. This response expressed as { *An*,x_n,*n* } is forwarded to the server by the client. The client calls *confirm* to ensure the correctness of the hash values after the modification of x_n. The client then calls the *consumers_modify*function for the retrieval of data from the modified block to enable verification of the correctness of the updations carried out on the PMT.

Data Insertion

The client inserts a new data block x*n** in the existing PMT with this operation. The client sends the "*renew* = *An, xn*, inc*" query to the server making a request for the insertion of a new node. In response to this, the server invokes*Incorp*()forthe reconstruction of the PMTafter insertion of *xn** with a new data block. The new leaf node *An∗* similar to*xn∗* is created and inserted into the tree after *An* as shown in Figure.5.5. Then the nodes *An* and *xn** are added as the left and right child nodes *An**. The server then invokes*modify*() for the updation of the hash values to be assigned to the new nodes *xn** and *An**.

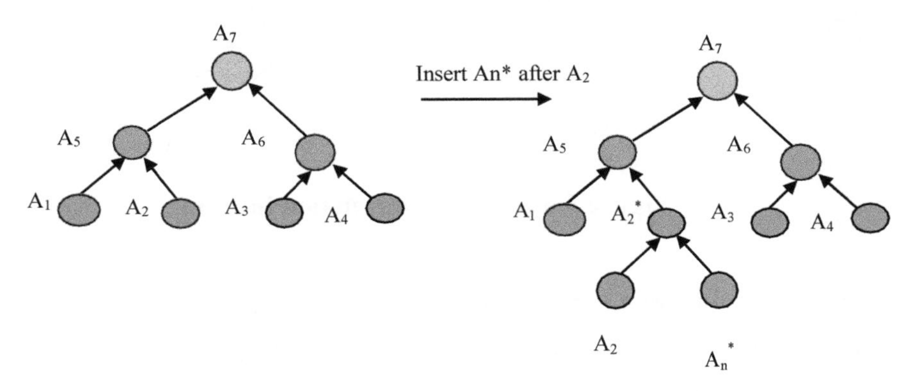

Figure 5.5 Data Block Insertion in PMT

The response { *xn, n, Aroot*} computed by the server is sent to the client who further invokes the function*verify*() to ensure the correctness of *xn* and *n*. If the components of the tuple *xn* and *n* are valid and match with the n^{th}node of the tree, the cost of the new root *Aroot*is computed by the client using*Incorp*()and compared with the actual value evaluated by the server.

Data Deletion

Data deletion is initiated by the client with a request toexecute the query *"restore = n, dlt"* to the server, following by which the nth data block is removed from the storage. The data blocks to the right of this block are shifted by 1 position towards left, such that the node *An*is transformed as *An -1*. As the location of *An+1* is modified, it is represented as *An -1* and incorporated with a new parent node. The server invokes the *Adjust(An-1,n,An+1)* function forrebuilding the tree after the deletion of node *An*. This process is illustrated in Figure 5.6.

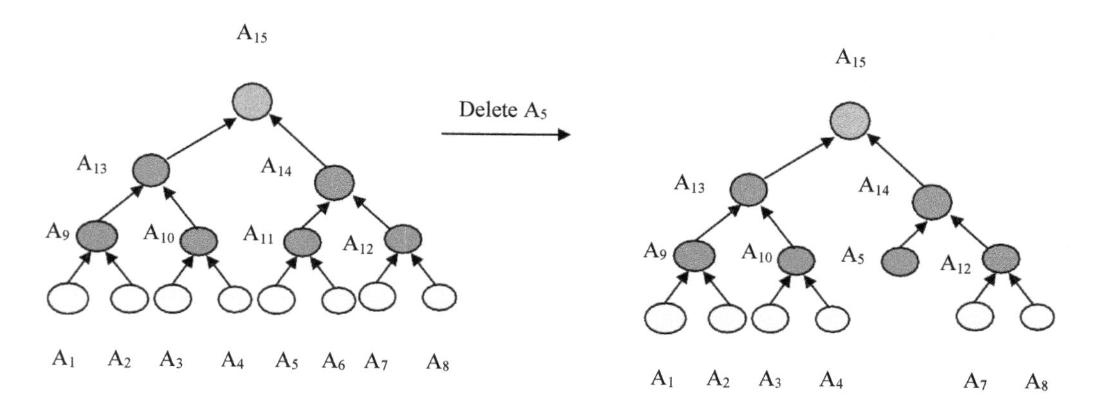

Figure 5.6 Data Block Deletion in PMT

As seen in Figure 5.6, the node *A5* is deleted from the tree. The node A6 now turns out to be the left child of *A11* and is assigned the label*A5*. The PMT is reordered such that the redundant node A11 is replaced by *A5*. On the deletion of a block from a tree, the client recomputes the cost of the root node and comparesit with that evaluated at the server to verify the correctness of the deletion operation.

5.5 EXPERIMENTAL RESULTS AND DISCUSSIONS

This section presents the experimental results and their interpretations through the exercise of the PMT based integrity verification system with well-defined test cases. For a fair comparison, the system is tested with test cases employed in the testing of the MHT and skip listbased system in chapter 3 and the FMT based system proposed in Chapter 4.

In addition, the performance of the system is evaluated with communication overhead and time complexity metrics for the dynamic client operations on data blocks of different sizes.

5.5.1 Experimental Setup

The multi-cloud environment for implementing the proposed system is deployed using Cloud Simulator, Google Drive, Dropbox and Cloud Me. The three phases of the protocol for data integrity check are implemented with the functions listed in section 5.4.1, in Java with Eclipse as front end.

Similar to sections 3 and 4, the size of the public and private keys is assumed as 160 bits. The smaller the key size, computations will be faster. However, they are susceptible to brute force attacks. Larger keys are highly secure but the computational time will be higher.

The experimental setup for accessing data from multi-cloud for rehabilitation services is shown in Figure 5.7. The patient data is distributed in storage devices distributed in multiple medical clouds in encrypted representation. The CSP supports encryption and decryption for protection of patient data. The data is accessible by multiple healthcare providers from the multiple clouds.

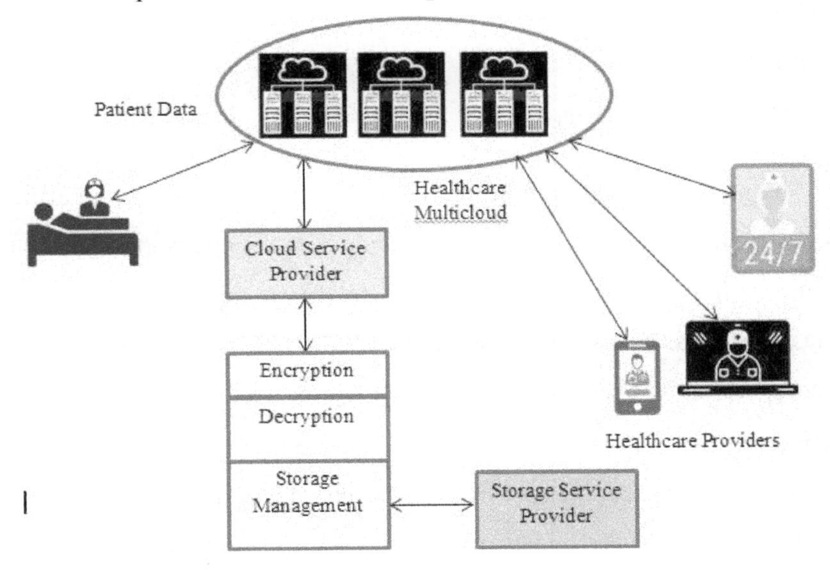

Figure 5.7 Multi-cloud Setup for Rehabilitation Services

5.5.2 Test cases and Results

The test cases and time taken for proof generation and verification operations are presented in this section.

Insertion

The following record was created and inserted into the file.

DeStart: 2014-01-15

Stop: 2015-10-05

Patient: 123e4567-e89b-12d3-a456-426785440000

Encounter: 123e4567-e89b-12d3-a456-325655440000

Code: 573621

Description: Albuterol 0.09 milli gram(mg)bronchodilators

Cost:20.43 USD

ReasonCode :195967001

Reason Description: Asthma

The node corresponding to the data block was inserted at an arbitrary location by reconstructing the PMT. The new hash values of the nodes in the authentication path were modified and the tuple $\{An.U, An.S, An.W\}$ was updated for each of these node *An*.The correctness of insertion was verified with a query of the *Description* field from the record, which was retrieved from the newly inserted block.

Updation

At the client-side, the *cost* field of the above record was modified to 19.10 USD. The updation was ensured by issuing a query of the *cost*, which returned the new value.

Deletion

This operation was tested by deleting all the records with *Code value 57362.* As a result of deletion, the PMT was reconstructed and the tuple $\{An.U, An.S, An.W\}$

was updated for each non-leaf node *An* affected by the deletion operations. A query issued to retrieve records with the above field value did not return any record.

The performance of the proposed algorithm was compared with that of the MHT and skip list based method and the FMT based method, with the same health care dataset. Details of thetime taken for the generation of authentication proofs and integrity checking are presented in Table 5.1.

Table 5.1 Comparison of Performance Metrics

Block Size (No. of Records)	**Merkle Tree with Skip List**		**Fractal Merkle Tree**		**Position Aware Merkle Tree (Proposed)**	
	Proof Generation (ms)	**Integrity Check (ms)**	**Proof Generation (ms)**	**Integrity Check (ms)**	**Proof Generation (ms)**	**Integrity Check (ms)**
16	8	11	5	7	1	4
32	17	19	13	15	9	11
64	27	31	23	26	13	19
128	86	107	76	94	59	67
256	140	180	132	171	115	123
512	398	415	385	395	360	377

Metrics used as visual interpretation, are illustrated in Figure 5.8. PMT based method is seen taking a lower computational time for all block sizes.

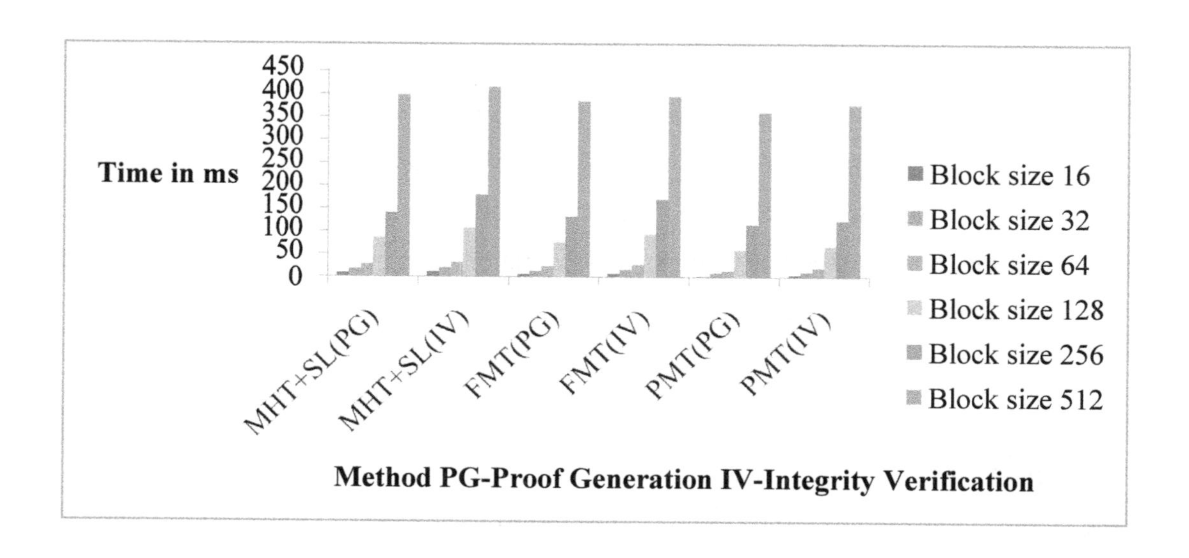

Figure 5.8 Comparative Analyses of Performance Metrics-Proof Generation and Integrity Check

5.5.3 Computational Complexity Analysis

The mathematical representation for complexity evaluation of the techniques employed in this research is summarized in Table 5.2., assuming N nodes in the respective tree structures. It is seen that space and communication complexity are very low for PMT. These notations are based on the empirical results reported in the literature. However, there may be minor deviations during the numerical evaluation of the complexities, due to the characteristics of the data.

Table 5.2 Storage and Communication Complexity Analysis

Methods	Complexity			Publicly Verifiable	Dynamic Operation Support
	Storage at client side	Storage at server side	Communication transparency		
Merkle Hash Tree	$O(1)$	$O(n)$	$O(1)$	No	Partial
Merkle Tree	$O(1)$	$O(n)$	$O(1)$	No	No
B+ Tree	$O(1)$	$O(n)$	$O(1)$	No	No
Fractal Merkle Tree	$O(1)$	*1.5 log2 N/loglogN*	*logN/loglogN*	Yes	Yes
Position Aware Merkle Tree	$O(1)$	$O(n)$	$O(\log n)$	Yes	Yes

The computational times for pre-processing, challenge creation and client authentication operations for different MT-based integrity verification methods were evaluated, details are provided in Table 5.3 and visually analysis for a fixed file size of 32 MegaByte(MB)ispresented in Figure 5.8. It is seen that the PMT method consumes lower computational times for various pre-processing, challenge creation and client authentication operations. Also, the time for dispute comparison is too small compared to the other two metrics as it involves only one mathematical operation. For a clear examination of all the metrics, the dispute creation time is scaled by a factor of 100 in Figure 5.9.

Table 5.3 Performance Metrics- Client-Side Computation

Methods	Pre-system Time (ms)	Dispute Creation (ms)	Client authentication (ms)
MHT	7441.3	3.7	1104.3
MT	7662.5	5.6	1206.2
B^+ Tree	7824.5	6.9	1402.3
FMT	7388.2	4.1	982.7
PMT	7366.2	3.2	350.7

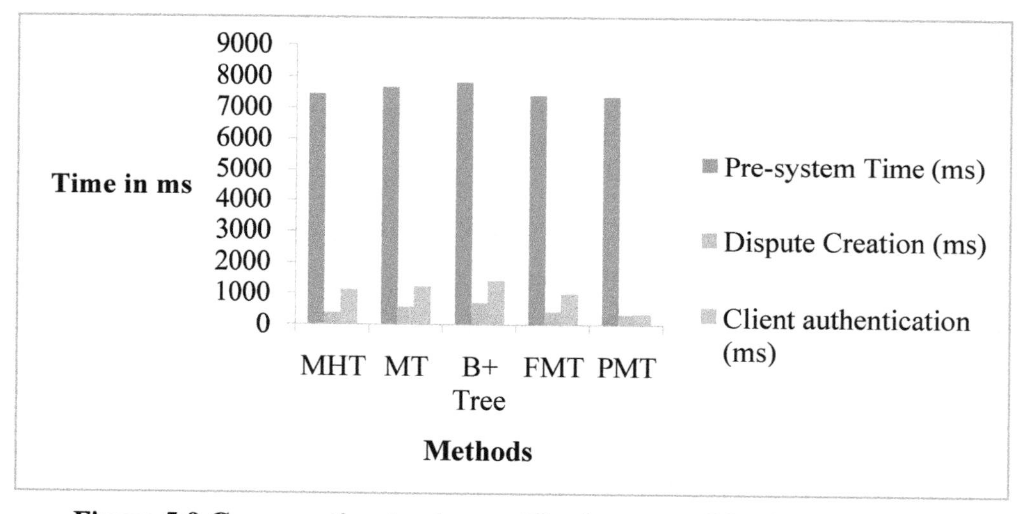

Figure 5.9 Comparative Analyses of Performance Metrics-Client-side Computation

Communication overhead is a vital metricused inassessing the quality of the integrity verification mechanism. The communication overheads for handling data blocks of sizes spanning 1KiloByte (KB) to 1024 KB are listed in Table 5.4. and these metrics are visually represented in Figure 5.10.

Table 5.4 Communication Overhead

Block Size (KB)	Communication Overhead				
	Merkle Hash Tree	Merkle Tree	B^+ Tree	FMT	Position Aware Merkle Tree
1	270.1	290.2	310.2	290.1	260.2
2	252.3	274.5	295.6	270.6	242.1
4	244.3	265.2	289.1	264.1	234
8	230.2	250.3	271.2	246.2	221.2
16	222.6	245.1	265.8	240.8	212.9
32	212.6	224.1	247.2	222.2	201.5
64	208.2	220.1	239.2	214.2	198.2
128	195.2	210.2	225.1	200.1	185.1
512	184.2	201.5	212	187	174.2
1024	172.5	192.5	201.8	176.8	162.3

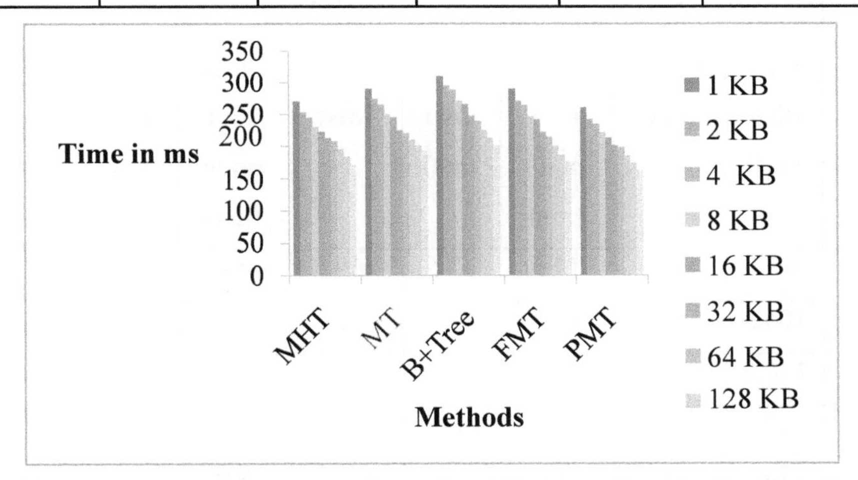

Figure 5.10 Comparative Analysis of Communication Overhead

Experimental results, show the PMT based integrity verification process exhibitingrelatively lower communication overheads, invariably for data blocks of different sizes.

5.5.4 Performance Evaluation for dynamic data operations

This section carries an exclusive analysis of the performance of the MT, FMT, and PMT on insertion, deletion and updation operations for different number of blocks. These operations were performed on a file of size 45 MB, synthetically generated with the Synthea software which contained around 4000 records in various categories that include allergies, patients, conditions, etc. Evaluation of the performance with respect to the number of records was done as the integrity verification required performance at the record and attribute levels corresponding to each patient in the medical cloud. Details of the computational times at the server and client ends for dynamic modification, insertion and deletion operations with the varying number of blocks are given in Table 5.5, Table 5.6 and Table 5.7 respectively.

Table 5.5 Computational Time Metrics-Data Modification

No. of Records	MT			FMT			PMT		
	User disp (ms)	Server (ms)	Client root node (ms)	User disp (ms)	Server (ms)	Client root node (ms)	User disp (ms)	Server (ms)	Client root node (ms)
32	69.1	311.3	14.5	48.5	260.8	8.4	28	210.3	4.2
64	105.3	503.3	14.4	84.7	452.8	8.3	64	402.3	4.1
128	140.9	915.2	15.4	120.3	864.7	9.3	100	814.2	5.1
256	162.3	302.3	14.9	141.7	251.8	8.8	121	201.3	4.6
512	175.2	501.2	15	154.6	450.7	8.9	134	400.2	4.7

Table 5.6 Computational Time Metrics -Data Insertion

No. of Records	MT			FMT			PMT		
	User disp (ms)	Server (ms)	Client root node (ms)	User disp (ms)	Server (ms)	Client root node (ms)	User disp (ms)	Server (ms)	Client root node (ms)
32	78	311	15.5	58	261	9.3	38	211	4.3
64	87	501.2	15.3	67	451.2	9.1	47	401.2	4.1
128	125	899.2	15	105	849.2	8.8	85	799.2	3.7
256	143	300.1	15.4	123	250.1	9.2	103	200.1	4.2
512	160	501.2	15.6	140	451.2	9.4	120	401.2	4.4

Table 5.7 Computational Time Metrics -Data Deletion

No. of Records	MT			FMT			PMT		
	User disp (ms)	Server (ms)	Client root node (ms)	User disp (ms)	Server (ms)	Client root node (ms)	User Disp (ms)	Server (ms)	Client root node (ms)
32	82	192	201	51	149	156	31	99	136
64	63	177	157	32	134	112	12	84	90
128	80	204	180	49	161	135	29	111	115
256	75	200	221	44	157	176	24	107	156
512	96	201	241	65	158	196	45	108	175

The above metrics indicate the better performance ofthe PMT based system compared to other MT-based methods for all the dynamic operations. Evaluation of the percentage of improvement wasdone for the server-side computations for the demonstration of the significance of the system. Details are provided in Table 5.8.

Table 5.8 Percentage of Improvement in PMT Compared to MT and FMT

No. of Records	Dynamic Operations					
	Modification		Insertion		Deletion	
	MT	FMT	MT	FMT	MT	FMT
32	32.44	19.36	32.15	19.16	48.44	33.56
64	20.07	11.15	19.95	11.08	52.54	37.31
128	11.04	5.84	11.12	5.89	45.59	31.06
256	33.41	20.06	33.32	19.99	46.50	31.85
512	20.15	11.20	19.95	11.08	46.27	31.65

For a clear elucidation of the improvement attained in PMT based integrity verification, the graphical representation of this measure is given in Figure 5.11 for modification, Figure 5.12 for insertion and Figure 5.13 for deletion operations.

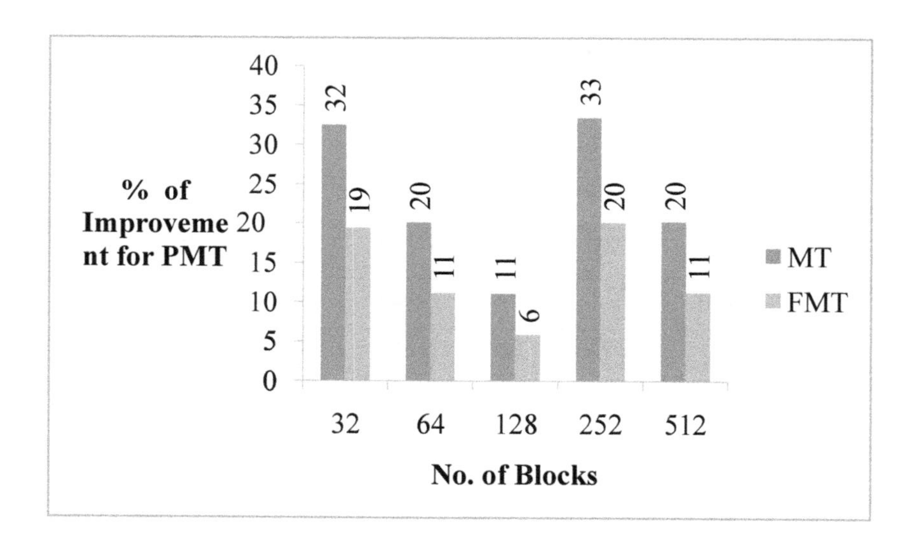

Figure 5.11 Percentage of Improvement in PMT –Data Modification

The above visual representation shows the percentage of improvement in PMT based integrity verification as around 20% compared to FMT based verification and 30% compared to MT-based verification for insertion operations. However, this improvement in percentage is seen as lower for a block size of 128 records and significantly higher for 256 and 512 records. This is attributed to the heterogeneity of the records in the blocks.

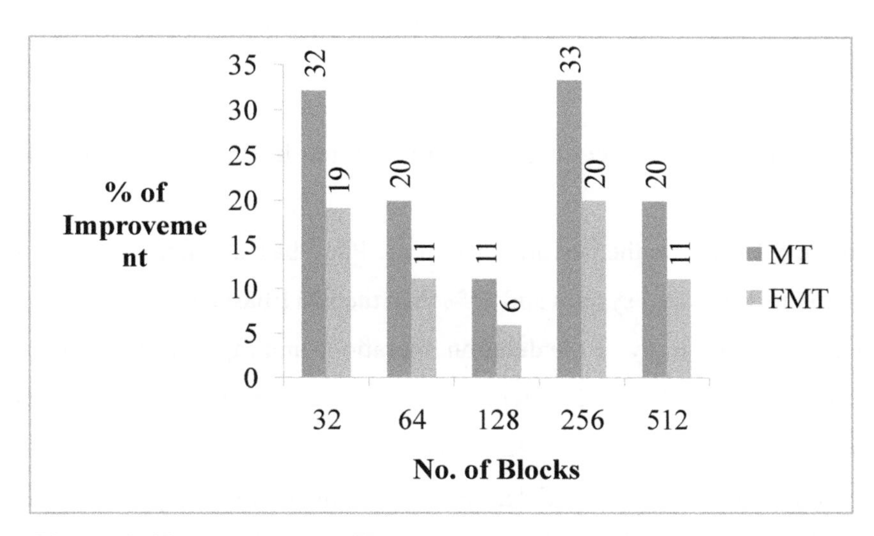

Figure 5.12 Percentage of Improvement in PMT –Data Insertion

Figure 5.12 depicts the improvement in the performance of the PMT based system with respect to insertion.The improvement percentage is seen as very close to that of the updation operation for all block sizes. The basic system architecture shows the similarity in the server operations for both updation and insertion operations. This is clearly evident from the similarity of server-side computation metrics for insertion and updation operations.

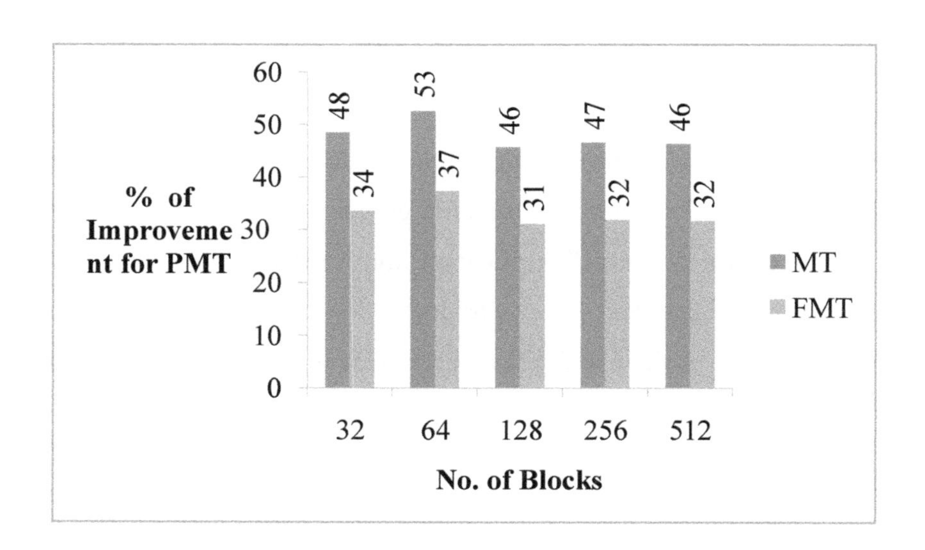

Figure 5.13 Percentage of Improvement in PMT –Data Deletion

Figure 5.13, shows the performance of the PMT based system as better around 50% compared to the MT-based system and 35% than the FMT based system. This enhancement is ascribed to the simplicity of the deletion operations and rapid reorganization of the tree when a node in the PMT based systemis deleted. The improvement is also seen as static for block sizes of 128, 256 and 512. This observation clearly reinforces the fact that reconstruction of a PMT, on node deletion is less cumbersome compared to that of MT and FMT.

Public verifiability is the significant feature of the PMT based integrity verification. The performance of this approach evaluated with respect to the time taken for public verification of the proofs in Table 5.9 for proof generation and integrity verification. This table presents a comparison of the proposed system with other publicly verifiable systems which demonstrates the superiority of the proposed system. Significant works on public auditability are performed by Mao [82&83] and Tian [84&85]. The performance metrics are generated from the existing works for the data set described in the experimental setup. The results are reported for block size of 512.

Table 5.9 Performance Comparison-PMT with Public Auditable Systems

Reference	Proof Generation (ms)	Integrity Check (ms)
Proposed Work	360	377
Mao et al. [82] (2017)	397	405
Mao et al. [83] (2017)	434	435
Tian et al. [84] (2017)	461	486
Tian et al. [85] (2019)	453	465

From the above table it is seen that best performance metrics are exhibited by the proposed system as it leverages the potential of the PMT for fast traversal of the nodes.

5.6 SUMMARY

This chapter has presented a PMT based novel integrity verification scheme, exploiting rapid ease of reconstruction in the verification of client data, under dynamic operations on data blocks. This system was implemented in a medical multi- cloud and exhaustively tested with suitable test cases. Well-designed experiments have been used in the evaluation of the computational times for proof generation and integrity verification. A detailed analysis of the experimental results has been presented to enable comprehension of the efficacy of the proposed PMT based verification scheme. The system is also evaluatedusing various performance metrics under all dynamic operations. The superiority of the system was demonstrated through a detailed comparison of the percentage of improvement, with respect to the most vital server-side computations, for all dynamic operations.

The proposed PMT based system exhibits the essential features and excellent performance metrics, highly warranted in a medical multi-cloud environment, in which services with a high degree of precision should be provided to the clients. The proposed PMT based verification system can be integrated with the existing cloud- based healthcare models easily, for enhanced rehabilitation solutions, irrespective of the heterogeneity of the underlying infrastructure, performance and resource constraints of the client devices.

CHAPTER 6

FULLY HOMOMORPHIC ENCRYPTION BASED DATA INTEGRITY ASSURANCE IN CLOUD STORAGE

6.1 INTRODUCTION

In the earlier three chapters, the security features of MHT, FMT, and position-aware MHT in implementing PDPs for dynamic integrity checks, in the most stringent and sensitive medical cloud environments have been demonstrated. Extensive experiments with the MHT and FMT based PDPs have proved their efficacy in the implementation of the data integrity check mechanism for insertion, deletion and updation operations at the attribute level, for data blocks of size ranging from 16 to 512 records, with low computational and storage complexities. In addition to the above intrinsic features, the ability to perform integrity checks by service providers and TPAs without revealing the original client data is the much sought after the requirement of data owners. Clients have anxiety about sharing sensitive health care and other personal data for integrity verification even with the most trusted entities. With the introduction of Homomorphic Encryption (HE) techniques this issue is resolved and a higher level of security is assured.

HE refers to the conversion of plain text into cipher text that enables the performance of all mathematical operations on the ciphertext. The security of client data in cloud storage is enhanced with the use of HE schemes. Cloud service providers allow data clients accessto the encrypted data from the cloud for intended applications without affecting the plain data. This feature also facilitates the resolution of nonrepudiation by the client and the server and simplifies integrity checking. While conventional integrity check mechanisms rely on the client-side data for integrity checks which require additional communication overheads, HE mitigates the need for this data.

With the implementation of three PDPs based on the MT, the need for protecting client data from accidental or intentional attacks has been perceived in this research work.AnFHE scheme for integrity protection of health care data in a multi- cloud environment has been proposed.

In this chapter, the FHE Scheme using Integers with smaller Key length (FHESIK) for verification of Advanced Encryption Standards (AES) circuits is presented. This scheme is tested with attributes in client data records in a medical cloud environment and compared with similar algorithms with respect to computational times. The choice of the homomorphic parameters has been chosen heuristic helping the establishment of the strength of the proposed system. The sections that follow contain an elaborate review of the homomorphic integrity check mechanisms, description of the working principles of the system, quantitative results, thorough result interpretation, and their implications. The objective results of experiments with well-designed test data show the suitability of, the proposed FHE system for implementing fine-grained integrity check mechanism which has the potential to scale to client records and files.

6.2 RELATED WORK

Rivest et al. [93] have conceptualized privacy homomorphism, the notion of applying mathematicalcomputations on encrypted data, protecting the original data.The authors have expressed concern over finding a highly secure privacy homomorphism, on a large set of operations on encrypted data.

Variants of FHE called Partial FHE, first-generation FHE, second-generation FHE, and third-generation FHE has been introduced based on the underling encryption approach. Partial FHE functions are homomorphic over a single operation. The RSA cryptosystem [97] is homomorphic for the multiplication operation. In this system, the product of two ciphertexts gives the encrypted form of the product of two plain texts. Similarly, the public-key cryptosystem of Paillier [98] is homomorphic in addition. Later, in 2008, the concept of somewhat homomorphism was introduced by Melchor et al. [99]. It indicates the support to both addition and multiplication on ciphertext, with a bound-on multiplication operation.

FHE function is an encryption function with high degrees of freedom which allows multiple mathematical computations on the encrypted data without constraints. The first FHE scheme based on lattice cryptography, supporting addition and multiplication operations on encrypted data was proposed by Gentry [94]. The authors employed bootstrapping for homomorphically decrypting the ciphertext which generates a new ciphertext for every encryption of the same plain text. Implementation of this system for a basic bit operation takes 30 minutes as reported in [95].

Dijk et al. [96] extended the basic FHE proposed in [94] to work with integers, which are conceptually simpler compared to computations with lattices. The security of this system is based on the concept of Approximate Greatest Common Divisor (AGCD), which recovers an integer p from several elements which are almost the multipliers of p. This approach is called the Dijk, Gentry, Halevi and Vaikuntanathan's (DGHV) method after the authors.

Later, this approach was improved by the quadric form of encryption employingsmall-sized public keys. Theapproach proposed in [101] has demonstrated the ability of FHE to accomplish with simple arithmetic operations on small integers. As an improvement of this technique, the authors have proposed a compression [101] scheme to considerably minimize the size of the public key in the DGHV method. This FHE scheme was implemented with a public key of size 10.1 MB compared to that of the 802 MB in the DGHV method. Modulus switching was further exploited in the levelled homomorphic encryption scheme called Brakerski-Gentry- Vaikuntanathan's (BGV) proposed in [104], which employed a complete ladder of moduli after each multiplication to scale down the ciphertext to the next modulus.

In recent years, cryptographic systems are built on the concept of Learning With Errors (LWE) [103], attributing to its difficulty in recovering secrets from n

number of linear equations. The scale-invariant scheme proposed by Brakerski [105] and the Ring-LWE of Fan and Vercauteren [104] is the widely used LWE scheme. An extended version of the LWE scheme in [105] for attribute-based encryption has been proposed in [103]. A scheme called the Scalable Homomorphic Implementation of Encrypted Data (SHIELD) proposed in [130] is a variant of the scheme proposed in [103] which performs computations on matrices, unlike the other LWE schemes which are based on vector computations. Though the cost of matrix operations is higher compared to that of vector operations, the cost of this scheme is lower due to a lack of relinearization.

Bootstrapped schemes with built-in capabilities to reduce the ciphertext noise without the need for explicit bootstrap operations proposed in [131,132,133,134] find extensive employment in integrity check mechanisms due to the security of the ciphertext, characteristic of these methods. A complete review of various HE schemes, and their variants has been presented in the seminal work of Bonnoron [135].

A detailed review of HE schemes shows FHE schemes as best suited for multi-cloud environments established with heterogeneous infrastructure, clients and services. Various works on the deployment of HE in the security mechanisms for cloud infrastructure are reported in the literature. Security issues in the cloud environment have been identified by Atayero and Feyisetan in [106] and HE based solutions are advocated, thanks to their data security and privacy.

The privacy concerns of clients in cloud environments are categorized as data privacy, function privacy, query privacy, and server privacy, all of which are achieved with the use of HE schemes. While data privacy is enforced in cloud-based solutions, other privacy needs are not addressed much. However, in special enterprise scenarios, in addition to data privacy, exclusive privacy requirements must be ensured to establish business integrity.

In financial applications, it is essential to protect the data and the transactions of the client. In this context, Asharov et al. [107] have proposed a threshold-based

FHE exhibiting low communication, computational and interaction overheads for computations involving multiple entities. The feasibility of providing function privacy using HE schemes have been evaluated in [108] by Naehrig et al. The authors demonstrate the possibility of realization of a HE based solution based on matrix algebra and multicore architecture for the achievement of function privacy.

Hu et al. [109] have shown the possibility of achievement of data and query privacy simultaneously with HE schemes. However, in this scheme, the query was represented as n components, each of which was encrypted. Though the security of the system improves with the number of components, the complexity of the system also increases simultaneously.

Unintentional access to partial or complete client data by unauthorized entities in the cloud environment called data leakageis a major security issue due to vulnerabilities in security mechanisms. Homomorphic methods find successful applications in mitigating data leakage [110] problems as the original data is encrypted by the client before outsourcing it to servers. Security requirements such as confidentiality, integrity, authenticity, and Multi-Party (MP) computation are accomplished with asymmetric cryptography. The best data integrity verification schemes can be realized through the integration of public-key cryptographic systems and FHE.

6.3 PROPOSED METHODOLOGY

The proposed system is based on the fundamental mathematical models of FHE and asymmetric cryptography. These concepts are described in the following subsections with illustrations, for a clear understanding of the architecture and functionalities of the proposed system.

6.3.1 Fully Homomorphic Encryption

As seen from the previous sections, FHE facilitates computations on encrypted data, protecting the integrity of the original data. Given a message

$m=(m_1,m_2,..m_n)$comprising n components, evaluation of a function f on m can be performed on $E_k(m)$and the result can be decrypted. The schematic of the FHE scheme depicting this process is shown in Figure 6.1. This process is described below.

For the plain text m, ciphertext C is generated as in Equation 6.1.

$$C= E_k(m) \tag{6.1}$$

When a client requests a server to evaluate a function f on the plain text m, it evaluates f on cipher text C, whichresults in a value equal to the encrypted value of $f(m)$as in Equation 6.2.

$$f(C)= E_k(f(m)) \tag{6.2}$$

The result of the computation $E_k(f(m))$is then sent to the client by the server. This value is deciphered using the decryption function D and the secret key k to get $f(m)$ as in Equation 6.3.

$$D_k(E_k(f(m)))=f(m) \tag{6.3}$$

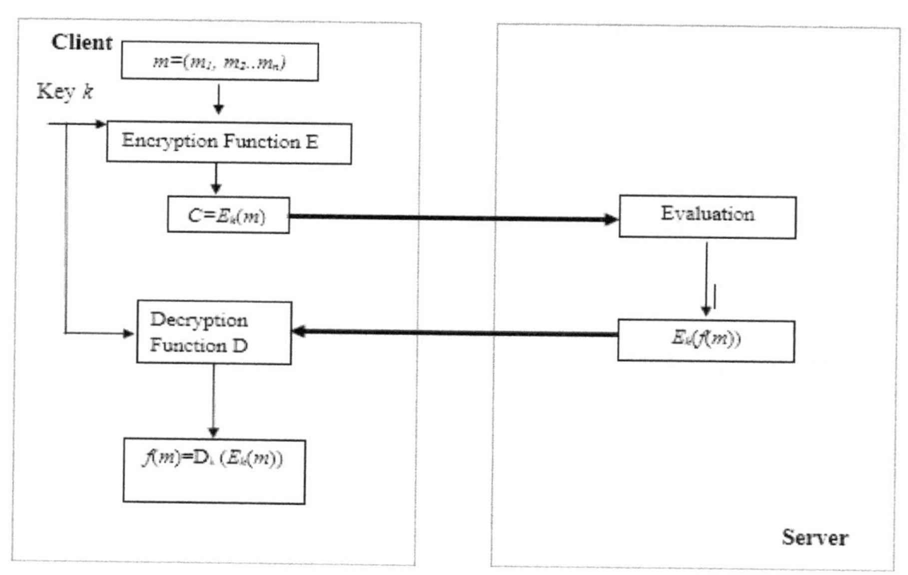

Figure 6.1 Fully Homomorphic Encryption

It is evident that the server performs computations on the encrypted data, from which the result of the computations on plain data is extracted by the client. Hence,

FHE is exploited by the clients in outsourcing sensitive data and mathematical calculations, demanding heavy computing and storage requirements.

6.3.2 Integrity Verification with FHE

In addition to providing confidentiality services, FHE can also be extended to the provision of integrity verification as shown in Figure 6.2. A verifiable FHE scheme is built by integrating verification features with HE, which enables clients to outsource complex computations on sensitive data to untrusted remote servers. The model for a Verifiable FHE (VFHE) first proposed by Genaro et al. [136], consists of three phases as described below for computation of a function f on client data.

Pre-processing

This is a one-time operation performed by the client on f tocompute the public and private values PU_f and PR_f respectively. The client shares the public information PU_f to the server and keeps PR_f private.

Input Preparation

When the client outsources the computation on a data b, it creates auxiliary public and private values PU_b and PR_b respectively on b andforwards PU_b to the server.

Output Computation and Verification

The server applies the function f on the public information pair $\{PU_f, PU_b\}$ to generate $f(b)$. It then computes a string πb, the encoded form of $f(b)$ and forwards it to the client. To verify the correctness of $f(b)$, the client computes $f(b)$ from π_b.

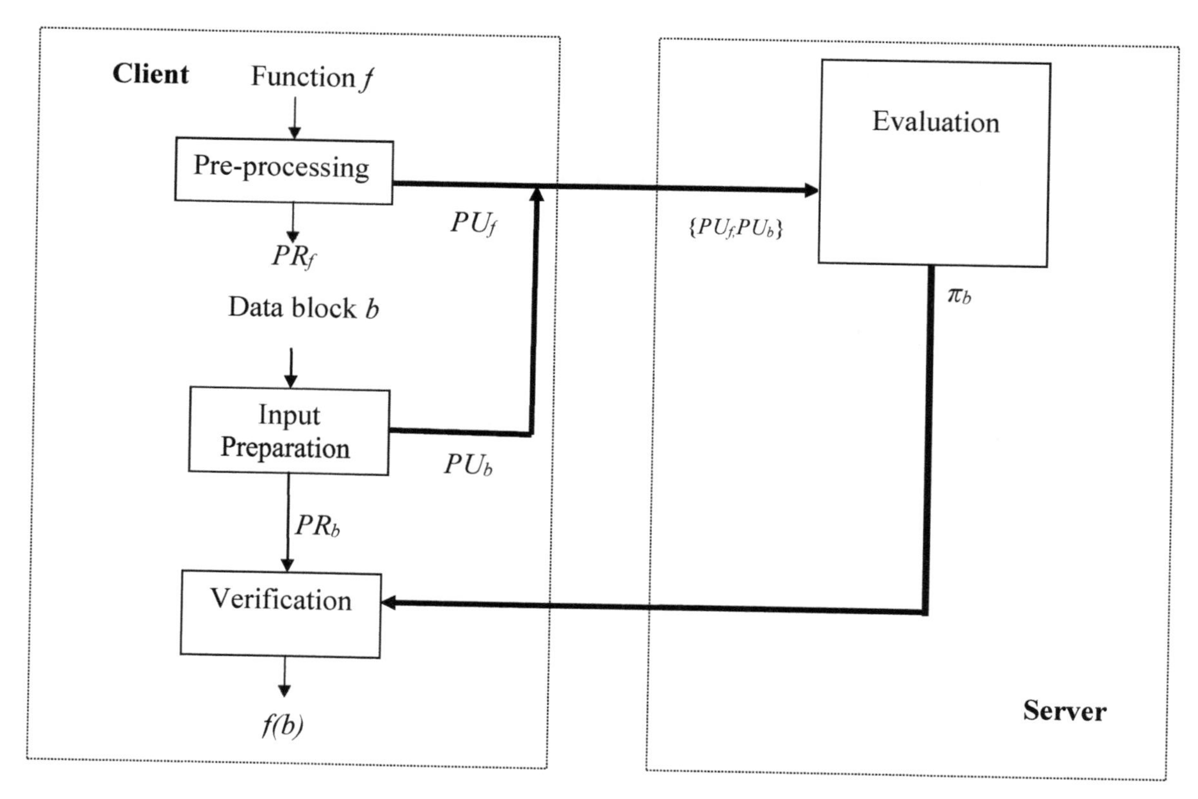

Figure 6.2 Verifiable Fully Homomorphic Encryption

It is seen that only a single message is exchanged by the client and server to each other in the verification process. As the interaction between the entities is minimized in the verification of computations, this mechanism is called non- interactive verifiable computing.

6.3.3 FHE on Integers

The elementary integer-basedFHE scheme proposed by Coron et al. [100] initially stores a subset of the public key and generates a complete public key by incremental multiplicative operations on the key sequences in four phases. The parameters employed in this scheme are listed below.

- λ is the security parameter
- γ is the bit-length of the each x_i
- η is the bit-length of the secret key
- ρ is the bit-length of the noise r_i
- τ is the number of elements x_i in the public key
- ρ'' is a secondary noise parameter for encryption

Each phase of the verification scheme is implemented as an exclusive function as indicated below.

KeyGen(1^λ) function generates public and private key pair from the security parameter λ

1. Generate a random prime number p such that $p \in [2^{\eta-1}, 2^\eta]$
2. Let $x_0 \leftarrow q_0.p$ where q_0 is a random integer in $[0, 2^\gamma/p]$
3. Generate integers x_{ib} for $1 \leq i \leq \beta$ and $b \in \{0,1\}$, where β is a random value

   $x_{ib} \leftarrow p.q_{ib} + r_{ib}$

   where q_{ib} are random integers in $[0, q_0]$ and r_{ib} are integers in $[2^{-p,} 2^p]$
4. Secret key $s_k \leftarrow p$ *public key* $p_k \leftarrow (x_0, x_{10}, x_{11}, \ldots x_{\beta 1}, x_{\beta 0})$

Evaluate(p_k,C,c_1,c_2...c_t) evaluates the addition and multiplication operation on each cipher text c_i for a cipher circuit C and returns the resultant integer.

Encrypt(p_k,m ∈ {0,1}) encrypts the binary message m into a ciphertext c

1. Choose a random subset S from $\{0,1,.. \tau\}$ and random integer r in $[2^{-p,} 2^p]$
2. Compute ciphertext c

$$c \leftarrow m + 2r + 2 \sum_{1 \leq i,j \leq \beta} b_{ij}\, x_{i0} x_{j1} \quad mod\ x_0$$

Decrypt(s_k,c) decrypts the ciphertext c into plaintext m with secret key s_k

$$m \leftarrow (c\ mod\ p)\ mod\ 2$$

The above scheme is employed in the proposed system for encryption and decryption onthe AES circuits.

6.3.4 Encryption and Decryption of Advanced Encryption Standards(AES) Circuits

The AES is a symmetric block cipher algorithm widely used in the encryption of sensitive data to be outsourced to remote servers. It can be implemented as an FHE scheme as it follows a block structure. From the structure of the AES encryption algorithm given in Figure 6.3, it is understood that the computations can be performed homomorphically on the AES cipher. The decryption of AES circuits is analogous to AES encryption with the same phase but in the reverse order

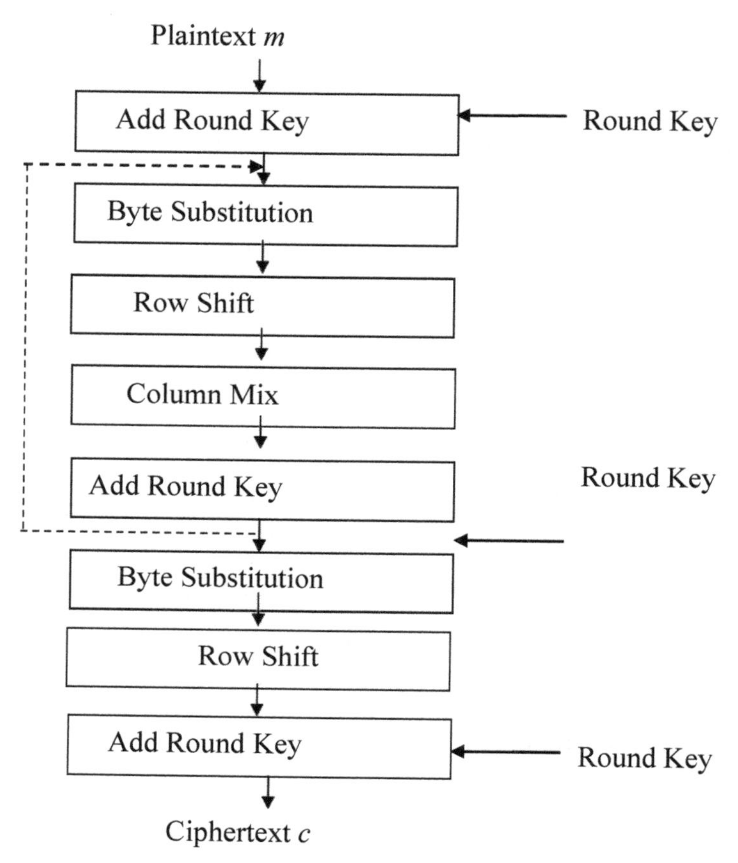

Figure 6.3 AES Encryption

6.4 ARCHITECTURE OF PROPOSED METHODOLOGY

This section presents the architecture of the proposed verifiable FHE integrity verification system for AES encryption, based on integer modulo operations. Each round of the AES encryption is realized as a set of logical gates, which can be evaluated homomorphically. The schematic of the proposed system for outsourced computations on AES encrypted data block b is given in Figure 6.4.The data block contains a sequence of blocks $b_1, b_2..b_n$. The required operations are performed on the encrypted data blocks at the server.

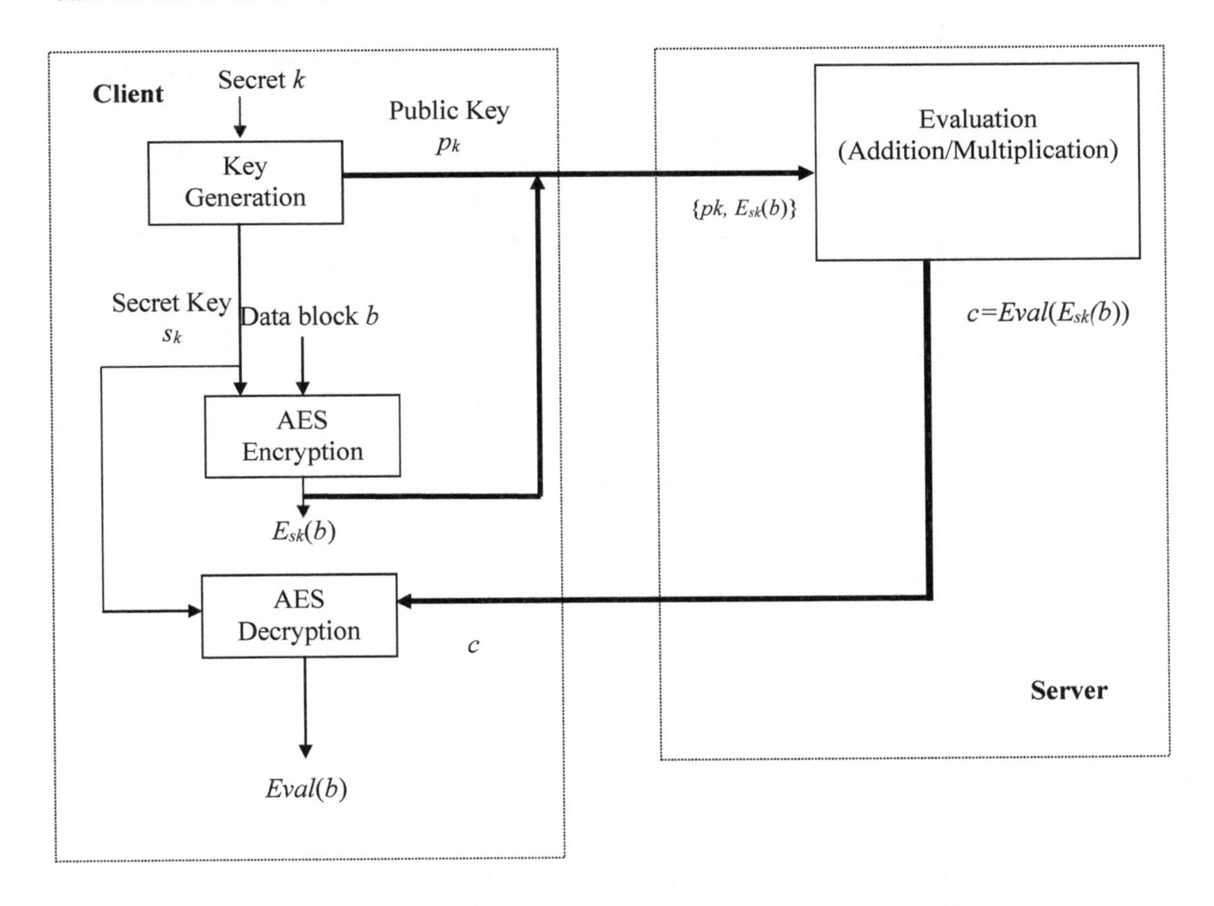

Figure 6.4 Fully Homomorphic Encryption of AES Encrypted Data

It is seen that the computations are performed with the minimal exchange of data between the client and the server. Only one message containing the public key and the AES circuit pair $\{p_k, c=E_{sk}(b)\}$ is sent by the client to the server. Also, the receiver sends only the result of the evaluation of the encrypted data for decryption by the client.

The FHE encryption scheme shown in Figure 6.4 can be extended for the verification of data integrity as illustrated in Figure 6.5. The algorithm for fully homomorphic integrity verification is given in Figure 6.6. and the flowchart depicting the same is shown in Figure 6.7.

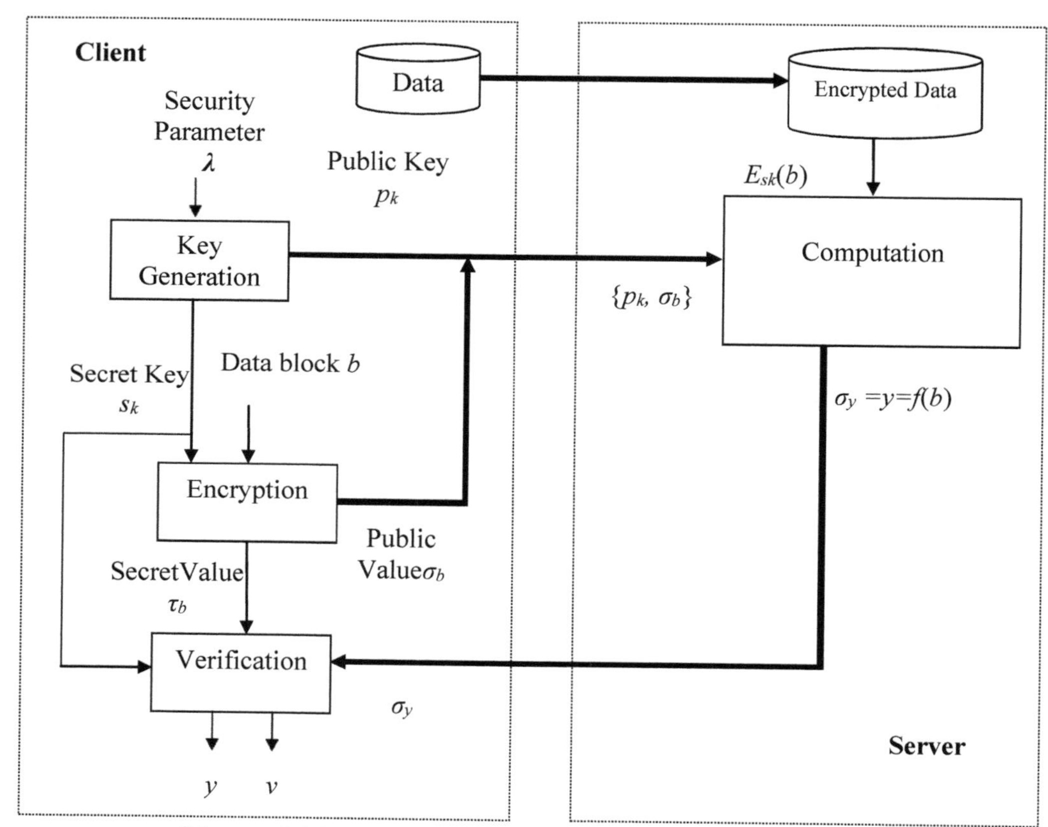

Figure 6.5 Fully Homomorphic Integrity Verification

Assuming that the original data is residing at the client and the encrypted data outsourced to the server, the integrity verification process verifies the correctness of the client data residing at the server. Assuming a security parameter λ at the client, public and private key pair $\{p_k, s_k\}$ is generated at the client-side. These values are characteristic of the homomorphic function f of the encrypted data. To verify the correctness of a block of data b, it is encrypted with the private key s_k to generate a pair of public and private components $\{\sigma_b, \tau_b\}$. The private component τ_b is maintained as a secret at the client and the public value σ_b is sent to the server.

The function f is applied on $E_{sk}(b)$, the encrypted value of b and the public value σ_b at the server. The function evaluates to a public value σ_y which is equivalent to the encoded value of $f(b)$. The value σ_y is sent to the server and decrypted at the client using the private values s_k and τ_b to get the value y and the binary verification code v. The value y is accepted by the client if v is *1* and rejected if v is *0*.

Input: Client data block b, Security Parameter λ
Output: output y, verification code v

Procedure:

1. *Generate the public-private key pair*
    a. $\{p_k, s_k\} \leftarrow KeyGen(\lambda)$
2. *Encrypt the data block bto generate public and private values at the client*
    a. $\{\sigma_b, \tau_b\} \leftarrow Encrypt(b, s_k)$
    b. *Send the public value* σ_b *to the server*
3. *Evaluate the function f on* σ_b *at the server to generate the public value* σ_y
    a. $\sigma_y \leftarrow f(\sigma_b, E_{sk}(b))$
    b. *send* σ_y *to the client*
4. *Generate y, the result of evaluation of f on b and verification code v*
    a. $\{v, y\} = decrypt(f(\sigma_b), s_k)$
    b. *if* $v \leftarrow 1$ *y is accepted by client*
        i. *else y is not accepted by client*
5. *End*

Figure 6.6 Algorithm for Fully Homomorphic Integrity Verification

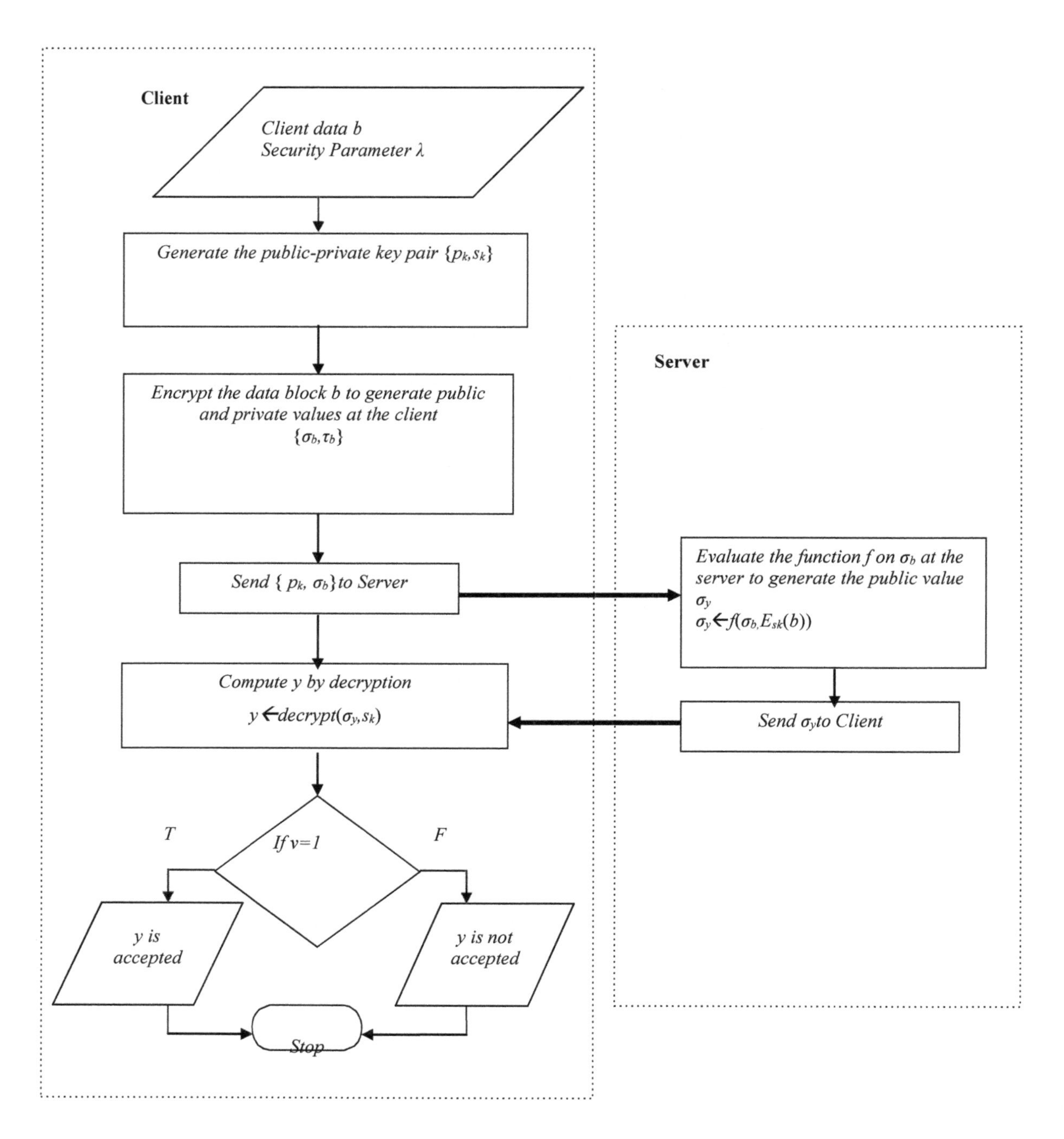

Figure 6.7 Flowchart for Fully Homomorphic Integrity Verification

The protocol architecture for the proposed system comprises the *KeyGen, Encrypt* and *Decrypt* functions given in section 6.3.3. The Evaluation functions for addition and multiplication operations on two plain texts m_1 and *m2* are given in equations (6.4) to (6.7).

add(E(m₁), E(m₂)

$$E(m_1)+E(m_2) = m_1+2r_1+pq_1+m_2+2r_2+pq_2 \quad (6.4)$$

$$= (m_1+m_2)+2(r_1+r_2)+(q_1+q_2)p \quad (6.5)$$

Mult(*E*(*m₁*), *E*(*m₂*)

$$E(m_1)*E(m_2) = (m_1+2r_1+pq_1)*(m_2+2r_2+pq_2) \quad (6.6)$$

$$= m_1 m_2+2(r_1 m_2+r_2m_1 + r_1 pq_2+r_2 pq_1) + p(m_1 q_2 +m_2q_1+pq_1 pq_2) \quad (6.7)$$

6.5 EXPERIMENTAL RESULTS AND DISCUSSION

The experimental results for homomorphic addition and multiplication operations on the encrypted data and their interpretations are dealt with in this section. A comparison of the computational times for the key operations for the proposed system and DGHV, BGV methods for the same data setis presented.

6.5.1 Experimental Setup

The proposed system was implemented with the Microsoft Simple Encrypted Arithmetic Library (SEAL).It is a collection of functions for homomorphic encryptions. It has a set of well-defined Application Programming Interfaces (API) for invoking the functions in a cloud environment. The cloud setup for the experiments is configured with Cloudsim and Google Drive.

6.5.2 Experimental Results

The experimental results were shown on health care records created with the Synthea software. Addition and multiplication operations are homomorphically performed on the 1163 encrypted patient records in a CSV file of size 235 KB. The experimental setup for testing the proposed homomorphic encryption system is shown in Figure 6.8. As seen from this figure, the patient data encrypted by HE mechanism is maintained by CSPs. The patient data is accessible by multiple health care providers. The encrypted patient data can be decrypted and accessible by the care givers. Further, modifications can be made by the healthcare providers by homomorphic operations, updating the patient history.

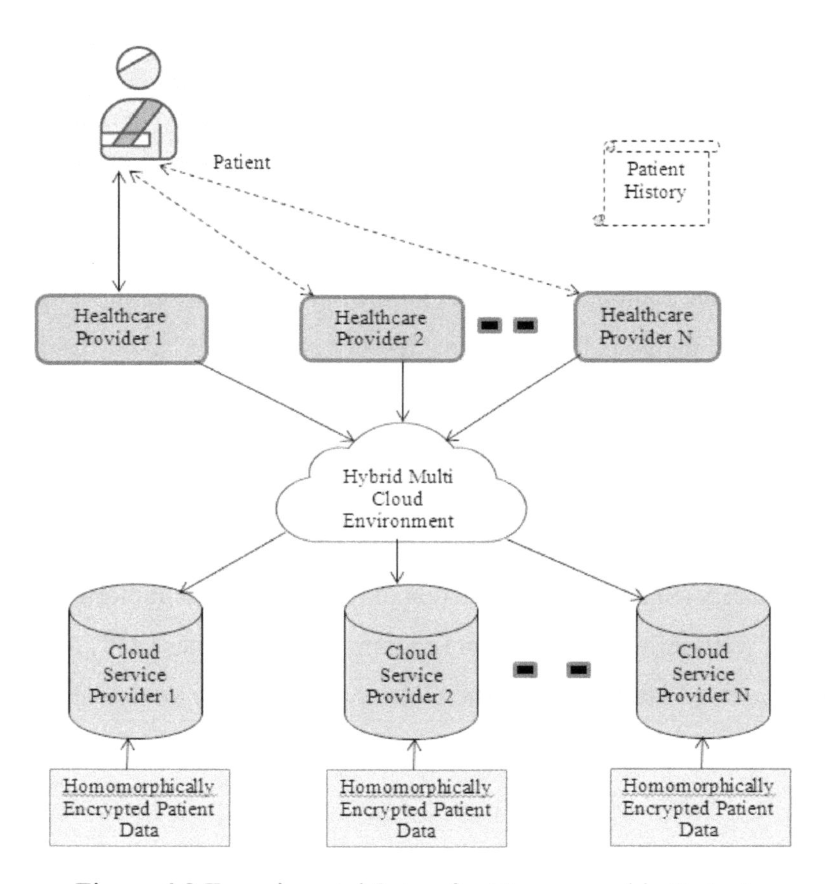

Figure 6.8 Experimental Setup for Homomorphic Data Access

Each patient record had 20 attributes listed in Table 6.1. These operations were performed on the entire patient record assuming the values for key parameters as in Table 6.2.

Table 6.1 Test Dataset structure

Attribute No.	Attribute Name
1	*Id*
2	*BIRTHDATE*
3	*DEATHDATE*
4	*SSN*
5	*DRIVERS*
6	*PASSPORT*
7	*PREFIX*
8	*FIRST*
9	*LAST*
10	*SUFFIX*
11	*MAIDEN*
12	*MARITAL*
13	*RACE*
14	*ETHNICITY*
15	*GENDER*
16	*BIRTHPLACE*
17	*ADDRESS*
18	*CITY*
19	*STATE*
20	*ZIP*

Table 6.2 Security Parameter Assumptions

Parameter	Description	Value
Λ	Security parameter	72
H	Bit-length of the secret key	2652
P	Bit-length of the noise	39
T	The number of integers in the public key.	6

The average computational times for addition and multiplication operations are given in Table 6.3 and 6.4 respectively.

Table 6.3 Computational Times for Addition

Scheme	**Key Generation (ms)**	**Encryption (ms)**	**Decryption (ms)**	**Evaluate (ms)**
DGHV [96] (2010)	8000	1320	1120	9140
BGV [104] (2012)	10300	180	130	6000
FHESIK with AES (Proposed)	3000	90	85	2000

Table 6.3 Computational Times for Multiplication

Scheme	Key Generation (ms)	Encryption (ms)	Decryption (ms)	Evaluate (ms)
DGHV [96] (2010)	11996	1581	1561	13695
BGV [104] (2012)	15446	901	850	14985
FHESIK with AES (Proposed)	4496	602	425	10190

The above tables,show the time taken for key operations as considerably low for both addition and multiplication operations on the AES circuits. It is also evident that the computational time for multiplication operation is higher than that of addition in all the methods. This increase is due to the number of computations involved in homomorphic multiplication operation as given in equation 6.7. For a clear interpretation, the visual representations of the computational times are shown in Figure 6.9 and 6.10 for addition and multiplication operations respectively.

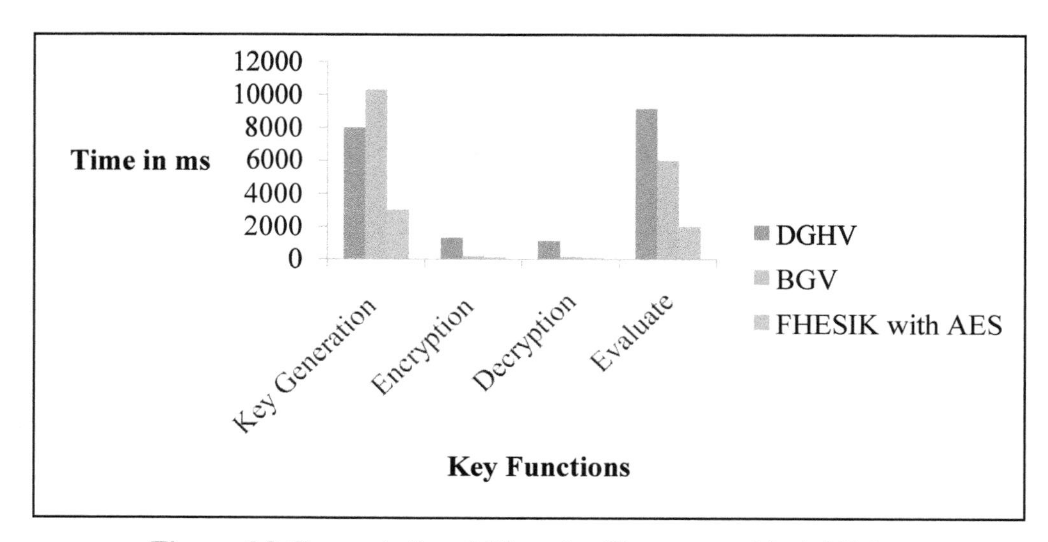

Figure 6.9 Computational Time for Homomorphic Addition

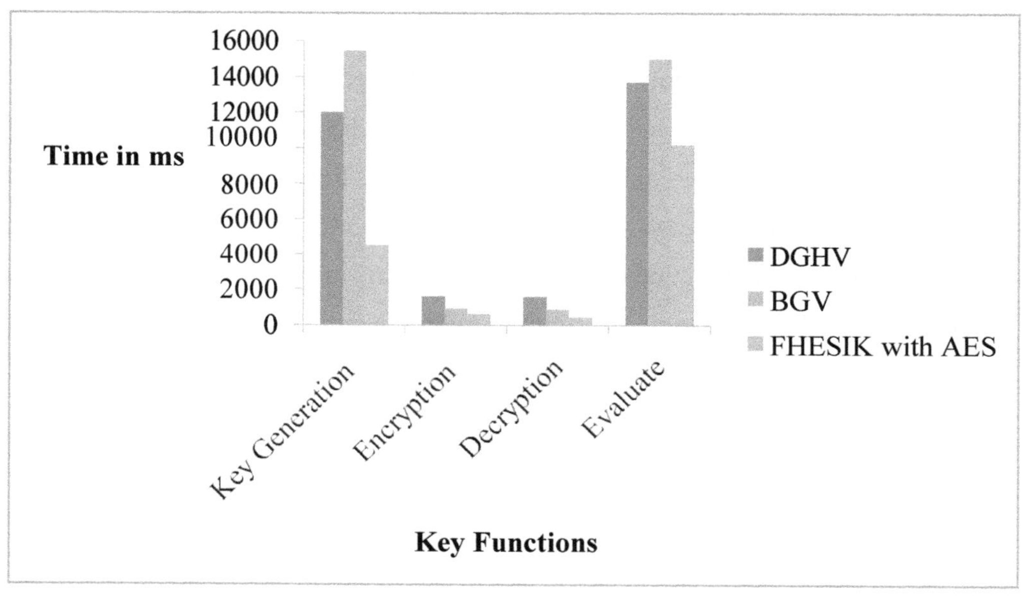

Figure 6.10 Computational Times for Homomorphic Multiplication

Despite the improvement in performance for FHESIK with AES from the statistical and graphical outputs being obvious, quantitative evaluation of thepercentage of improvement over other methods has been done and shown in Figure 6.11.

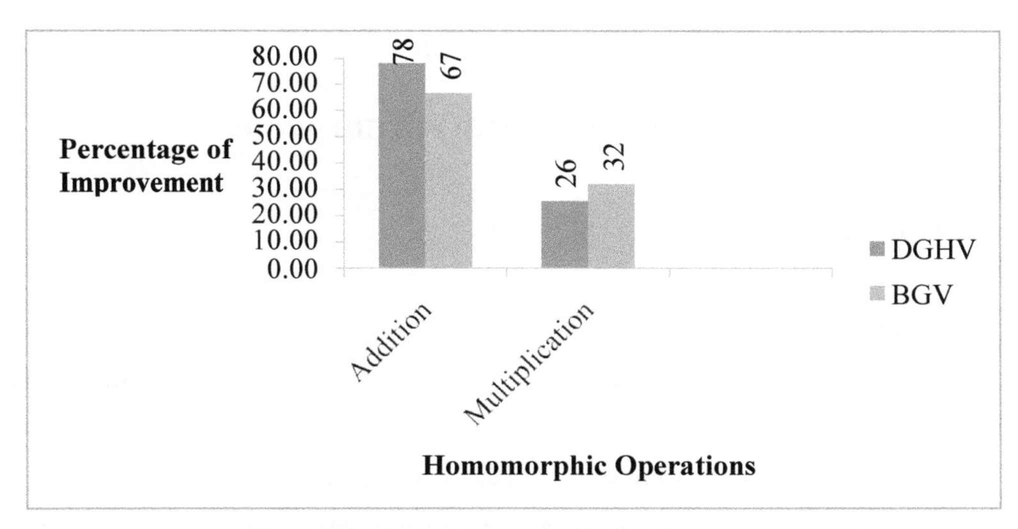

Figure 6.11Improvements in Performance

An enhancement by more than 60% for addition operations and more than 25% for multiplication operations is observed in the proposed system compared to the BGV and DGHV methods.

6.6 SUMMARY

Realizing the need for securing client data outsourced to remote cloud servers, this chapter has presented a novel homomorphic scheme for secured computation and integrity verification of patient data in a medical cloud. These operations on the evaluation of AES addition and multiplication circuits were tested for the demonstration of the security of the proposed integrity verification mechanism on sensitive patient records. Evaluation of computational times for various key operations of the protocol with a benchmark dataset highlights the superiority of the proposed system. It can be scaled down to enable verification of the integrity of the individual attributes of a patient or the entire file pertaining to a healthcare provider. The proposed homomorphic mechanism coupled with the PDPs based on MHT can add a new dimension to medical cloud security, anonymizing the computations and simplifying the integrity verification process for rapid healthcare solutions.

CHAPTER 7

CONCLUSION AND FUTURE WORK

7.1 CONCLUSION

This research work is aimed at the design and analysis of data integrity verification schemes for multi-cloud environments.The initial focus wason designing dynamic PDPs based on efficient tree-based data structures. The PDPs implemented using MHT, skip lists, FMT and PMT were subject to extensive testsin a simulated multi-cloud with dynamic record insertion, deletion and modification operations on healthcare records with well-designed test cases.

The PDP based on FMT simplifies the localization of tampering by traversal of the authentication paths. The experimental results show the excellent features of the proposed FMT based PDP performance with proof generation and integrity verification. The lower space and computational complexities are indicative of its pertinencein designing prospective solutions in the dynamic healthcare environmentfor the rapid delivery of healthcare services. Due to its simplicity, this model can be coupled with any heterogeneous cloud infrastructure with enthralling security requirements.

The proposed PMT based system exhibits the very essential features and excellent performance metrics, highly desirable in a medical multi-cloud environment, which requires the provision of accurateservices to the clients. This model can also be added to theworkflow of healthcare models for enhanced rehabilitation solutions, without any regard to the disparity of the cloud infrastructure and limitations of the client devices.

This research work can be extended to secure client data outsourced to remote cloud servers, employing a novel homomorphic scheme for protecting clinical data and verification of their intactness in a medical cloud. These operations tested on the AES encryption function demonstrate the security of computations on sensitive data.

7.2 FUTURE WORKS IN DATA INTEGRITY VERIFICATION

Thanks to the flexibility and cost-effectiveness of cloud-based solutions, many business enterprises, and service organizations are motivated to host their services in the cloud environment. Many essential services such as education, healthcare, hospitality, etc. are centred on cloud service models. There is still a great demand for intriguing services by clients from the service providers. The recent cloud service models are based on the design aspects ascribing to captivating the clients.

Simultaneously, data integrity verification schemes are also improvised to enable alignment with the complexity of these services. The recent trends in cloud computing and enhancements required in the integrity verification schemes give a clear direction on the future research prospects as below.

7.2.1 Re-outsourcing data detection

Service providers tend to re-outsource data to other service providers with an increase in client population. SLAs do not permit such outsourcing without consent from the client. Detection of re-outsourcing of data is an important requirement of data integrity in a multi-cloud environment. This activity can be curtailed through the use of fast and efficient block verification schemes that can rapidly access client data, generate proofs and verify them.

7.2.2 Deduplication

Client data is distributed as redundant copies across multiple storage devices to ensure the availability of data. The process of detection and deletion of duplicated copies of data, called deduplication, reduces the storage cost. Integrity verification protocols should operate on authentic updated versions of data to ensure the intactness of data. The existing deduplication schemes are discrete procedures applied before the integrity verification process. These approaches compare the data with copies existing at the storage and remove duplicate data. These comparisons are performed with hash values of data to reduce the time involved in the comparison. Integrating deduplication as a part of the data verification mechanism, redundant copies can be destroyed before the verification process, enhancing the performance of the verification process.

7.2.3 Assured deletion

Clients have the privilege of deleting datafrom remote servers. The deletion of data must be done to ensure no copies prevail in any of the storage devices. Incomplete deletion of multiple copies of data will result in security breaches, and ambiguity in business transactions, etc. Guarantee of the complete deletion of data called assured deletion or self-destruction is an important requirement in multi-cloud environments. This feature can be ensured through the employment of suitable data structures with efficient traversal algorithms, distributed and linked across multiple storage devices.

7.2.4 Self-controlling objects (SCO)

Sensitive data can be protected from adversaries by encapsulating them with the functions which manipulate them, such that the functions are invoked through well-defined interfaces. These encapsulated data objects are called Self Controlling Objects (SCO). Integrity mechanisms involve numerous computations with data during the verification process. While homomorphic functions operating on encrypted data cannot modify the original data, SCOs of unencrypted data can be manipulated by the functions without affecting the data elements. This kind of representation also simplifies the implementation of integrity verification algorithms.

7.2.5 Location verification

The client data residing in a device at a geographical location can be migrated by the service provider without the knowledge of the client, breaking the SLA. Service providers normally resort to this practice when the servers at a particular geographical location are overloaded or crashed. At times, they also migrate to enable a reduction in the cost of data access from a remote location. Ensuring the geographical location of data with granular attributes such as country, state, district, time zone, etc. is also an essential requirement of data integrity. Geographical location-aware data integrity mechanisms can help to track the location of data to ensure their intactness with respect to a predefined position. Position aware data structures can be employed for the accomplishment of these requirements.

7.2.6 Computational assurance

It is the practice of assuring the integrity of various processes involved in the storage, retrieval, and processing of data. It also ensures the trustworthiness of hardware components on which the computations are performed. It is also concerned with the security of cryptographic algorithms and the problem of attacks posed on them. This is one of the most complex requirements of an integrity verification mechanism, which can be accomplished by building an integral protocol based on the functionalities of various entities in a cloud environment.

The focus of this research work ison access to private health care records in a multi-cloud environment, realizing the objectives of deploying PDPs. The security mechanisms proposed in this research can be extended through the infusion of the above requirements. The outcomes of this research can be further optimized for resource-constrained devices, enabling the clients the facilityof direct exercise of control over their health records.

In addition to data integrity, authentication and confidentiality attacks, cloud-based data access mechanisms are highly susceptible to non-repudiation attacks by the client and server which have notbeen explored much. The FMT based PDP model implemented in this research also supports the detection of both client and server-side non-repudiation as part of the integrity verification process. This feature is very significant for multi-cloud environments, where there is a high likelihood of repudiations as multiple clients, service providers, TPAs and followers are involved. Further investigations of these origins of these attacks in such a heterogeneous environment can be taken upand breaches can be eliminated by strengthening the proposed FMT based PDP model.

There is a persistent demand for healthcare services across the globe, which requires very frequent access to health records, clinical data, real-time health parameters, historical records, etc. Delivery of these services can be regulated with faster retrieval of data-enabled with the use of position-aware search mechanisms. The PMT based PDP has demonstrated excellent performance with dynamic operations. This system can be extended to the support of the retrieval and verification of data from widely distributed storage devices across disparate geographical locations.

Above all, the FHE scheme for AES encryption proposed in this research can be extended to other classic and modern cryptographic algorithms and integrated with the PDP models for complete protection of client data.

Starting with the formulation of a significant problem for investigation, this research culminates with the demonstration of promising security solutions in cloud environments, identification of extension aspects for new functionalities and finding new prospects for potential enhancements. Though the research objectives are attained as demonstrated by the realistic outcomes, further investigations aligned with the impending enhancements will be of help in getting innovative solutions for mankind.

REFERENCES

1. A. Fox, R. Griffith, A. Joseph, R. Katz, A. Konwinski, G. Lee, D. Patterson, A. Rabkin and I. Stoica, *Above the Clouds: A Berkeley View of Cloud Computing*, [online] Technical Report No. UCB/EECS-2009-28 Available at http://www.eecs.berkeley.edu/pubs/techrpts/2009/eecs-2009-28.html.
2. E. Knorr and G. Gruman, *What Cloud Computing Really Means*, Infoworld, Electronic Magazine, [online] Available at http://www.infoworld.com/ article/ 08/04/07/ 15fe-cloud-computing-reality1.html.
3. B. Calder, J.Wang, A. Ogus, N. Nilakantan, A. Skjolsvold, S. Mckelvie, Y. Xu, S. Srivastav, S. Wu, S. Simitci and J. Haridas, *Windows Azure Storage: A Highly Available Cloud Storage Service with Strong Consistency*, Proceedings of the 23rd ACM Symposium on Operating systems Principles, ACMSOP-11, (2011),143-157.
4. H. Al-Aqrabi, L. Liu, J. Xu, R. Hill, N. Antonopoulosand Y. Zhan, *Investigation of IT Security and Compliance Challenges in Security-as-a-Service for Cloud Computing*,Proceedings of the IEEE 15th International Symposium on Object/Component/Service-Oriented Real-Time Distributed Computing Workshops, ISOCSRD -12, (2012), 124-129.
5. S. Nepal, S. Chen, K.J. Yaoand D. Thilakanathan, *DIaaS*: *Data Integrity as a Service in the Cloud*, Proceedings of the 4th IEEE International Conference on Cloud Computing, CLOUD-11, (2011), 308-315.
6. T. Ristenpart, E. Tromer, H. Shachamand S. Savage, *Hey, You, get off of My Cloud: Exploring Information Leakage in Third-Party Compute Clouds*, Proceedings of the16th ACM Conference on Computer and Communications Security, (2009), 199-212.

7. B. Chen, R. Curtmola, G. Ateniese and R. Burns, *Remote Data Checking for Network Coding-Based Distributed Storage Systems*, Proceedings of the ACM Workshop on Cloud Computing Security Workshop, ACMCCS-10, (2010),31-42.
8. G. Ateniese, S. Kamara and J. Katz, *Proofs of Storage from Homomorphic Identification Protocols*, Proceedings of the 15thInternational Conference on the theory and Application of Cryptology and Information Security, ASIACRYPT- 09, (2009), 319-333.
9. B. Wang, B. Liand H. Li, *Knox:Privacy-Preserving Auditing for Shared Data with Large Groups in the Cloud*, Proceedings of the 10th International Conference on Applied Cryptography and Network Security, ACNS-12, (2012), 507-525.
10. C.C. Erway, A. Kupcu, C. Papamanthou and R. Tamassia, *Dynamic Provable Data Possession*, Proceedings of the 16thACM Conference on Computer and Communications Security, CCS-09, (2009), 213– 222
11. Ł. Krzywiecki and M. Kutyłowski, *Proof of Possession for Cloud Storage Via Lagrangian Interpolation Techniques*, Proceedings of the 6thInternational Conference on Network and System Security, NSS-12, (2012), 305-319.
12. F. Rashid, A. Miri and I. Woungang, *Proof of Retrieval and Ownership Protocols for Enterprise-Level Data Deduplication*, Proceedings of the Conference of the Centre for Advanced Studies on Collaborative Research, CCAS-13, (2013),81-90.
13. Y. Zhu, H. Hu, G.J. Ahn and M. Yu, Cooperative Provable Data Possession for Integrity Verification in Multi-cloud Storage, *IEEE Transactions on Parallel and Distributed Systems*, **23**(12)(2012), 2231-2244.
14. Q. Zheng, and S. Xu, *Secure and Efficient Proof of Storage with Deduplication*, Proceedings of the 2nd ACM Conference on Data and Application Security and Privacy, ACMDASP-12, (2012), 1-12.
15. D. Cash, A. Küpçü and D. Wichs, Dynamic Proofs of Retrievability Via Oblivious RAM, *Journal of Cryptology*, **30**(1) (2017), 22-57.

16. B. Chen and R. Curtmola, *Robust Dynamic Remote Data Checking for Public Clouds*,Proceedings of the ACM Conference on Computer and Communications Security, ACMCCS-12, (2012),1043-1045.
17. E. Shi, E. Stefanov and C. Papamanthou, *Practical Dynamic Proofs of Retrievability*,Proceedings of the ACM SIGSAC Conference on Computer & Communications Security, ACM SIGSAC CCS-13, (2013), 325-336.
18. Y. Yu, J. Ni, J. Ren, W. Wu, L. Chen and Q. Xia, *Improvement of a Remote Data Possession Checking Protocol from Algebraic Signatures*, Proceedings of the International Conference on Information Security Practice and Experience, (2014), 359-372.
19. H. Wang and Y. Zhang, On the Knowledge Soundness of a Cooperative Provable Data Possession Scheme in Multicloud Storage, *IEEE Transactions on Parallel and Distributed Systems*, **25**(1) (2013), 264-267.
20. R. Chow, P. Golle, M. Jakobsson, E. Shi, J. Staddon, R. Masuoka and J. Molina, *Controlling Data in the Cloud: Outsourcing Computation without Outsourcing Control*, Proceedings of the ACM Workshop on Cloud Computing Security, (2009), 85-90.
21. D. Zissis and D. Lekkas, Addressing Cloud Computing Security Issues, *Future Generation Computer Systems*, **28**(3)(2012), 583-592.
22. R.V. Rao and K. Selvamani, Data Security Challenges and its Solutions in Cloud Computing, *Procedia Computer Science*, **48** (2015), 204-209.
23. M.G. Avram, Advantages and Challenges of Adopting Cloud Computing from an Enterprise Perspective, *Procedia Technology*, **12** (2014), 529-534.
24. Y. Tang, P.P. Lee, J.C. Lui and R. Perlman, *FADE: Secure Overlay Cloud Storage with File Assured Deletion*, Proceedings of the International Conference on Security and Privacy in Communication Systems, CCPCS-10, (2010),380-397.
25. A. Duncan, S. Creese and M. Goldsmith, An Overview of Insider Attacks in Cloud Computing, *Concurrency and Computation: Practice and Experience*, **27**(12) (2015), 2964-2981.

26. M.T. Khorshed, A.S. Ali and S.A. Wasimi, *Trust Issues That Create Threats for Cyber Attacks in Cloud Computing*, Proceedings of the 17th IEEE International Conference on Parallel and Distributed Systems, (2011), 900-905.

27. M.A. Hatef, V. Shaker, M.R. Jabbarpour, J. Jung and H. Zarrabi, HIDCC:A Hybrid Intrusion Detection Approach in Cloud Computing, *Concurrency, and Computation: Practice and Experience*, **30**(3) (2018), 1-10.

28. M.R. Mesbahi, A.M. Rahmani and M. Hosseinzadeh, Reliability and High Availability in Cloud Computing Environments: A Reference Roadmap, *Human-Centric Computing, and Information Sciences*, **8**(1) (2018), 1-31.

29. H. Abelson, R. Anderson, S. M. Bellovin, J. Benaloh, M. Blaze, W. Diffie, J. Gilmore, P.G. Neumann, R.L. Rivest, J.I. Schiller and B. Schneier, *The Risks of Key Recovery, Key Escrow, and Trusted Third-Party Encryption,* [online] Available at https://academiccommons.columbia.edu/doi/10.7916/d8gm8f2w, (1997).

30. L.J. Nieuwenhuis, M.L. Ehrenhard and L. Prause, The Shift to Cloud Computing: The Impact of Disruptive Technology on the Enterprise Software Business Ecosystem, *Technological Forecasting and Social Change*, **129** (2018), 308-313.

31. N. Ghosh and S.K. Ghosh, *An Approach to Identify and Monitor SLA Parameters for Storage-as-a-Service Cloud Delivery Model*, Proceedings of the IEEE Globecom Workshops, GLOBECOM-12, (2012), 724-729.

32. D. Birk and C. Wegener, *Technical Issues of Forensic Investigations in Cloud Computing Environment,*Proceedings of the 6*th* IEEE International Workshop on Systematic Approaches to Digital Forensic Engineering, (2011), 1-10.

33. J. Li, Y. Zhang, X. Chen and Y. Xiang, Secure Attribute-Based Data Sharing for Resource-Limited Users in Cloud Computing, *Computers & Security*, **72**(2018), 1-12.

34. Y. Deswarte, J.J Quisquater and A. Saïdane, *Remote Integrity Checking*, In Book Series IFIP International Federation for Information Processing-Integrity and Internal Control in Information Systems VI, 140 (2004),1-11.

35. S. Han, S. Liu, K. Chen and D. Gu,*Proofs of Retrievability Based on MRD Codes*, Proceedings of the International Conference Information Security Practice and Experience, ISPEC -2014, (2014), 330–45.

36. G. Ateniese, R. D. Pietro, L. V. Mancini and G. Tsudik, *Scalable and Efficient Provable Data Possession*, Proceedings of the 4th International Conference Security and Privacy in Communication Networks, Securecomm-08, (2008),1-10.

37. G. Ateniese, R. Burns, R. Curtmola, J. Herring, L. Kissner, Z. Peterson and D. Song, *Provable Data Possession at Untrusted Stores*, Proceedings of the 14th ACM Conference on Computer and Communications Security, CCS-07, (2007), 598-609.

38. J. Yuan and S. Yu, *Proofs of Retrievability with Public Verifiability and Constant Communication Cost in Cloud*, Proceedings of the International Workshop on Security in Cloud Computing, IWSC-13, (2013), 19–26.

39. R. Curtmola, O. Khan, R. Burns and G. Ateniese, *MR-PDP: Multiple-Replica Provable Data Possession*, Proceedings of the 28th International Conference on Distributed Computing Systems, (2008), 411-420.

40. Y. Zhang and M. Blanton, *Efficient Dynamic Provable Possession of Remote Data Via Balanced Update Trees*, Proceedings of the 8th ACM SIGSAC Symposium on Information, Computer and Communications Security, ACM SIGSAC CCS-13, (2013),183-194.

41. E. Esiner, A. Kachkeev, S. Braunfeld, A. Küpçü and O. Özkasap, *Flexdpdp: Flex List-Based Optimized Dynamic Provable Data Possession*, Cryptology Eprint Archive, Report 2013/645. Available at: https://eprint.iacr.org/2013/645 .

42. Y. Dodis, S. Vadhan and D. Wichs, *Proofs of Retrievability Via Hardness Amplification*, Proceedings of the Theory of Cryptography Conference, (2009), 109-127.

43. K. D. Bowers, A. Juels and A. Oprea, *Proofs of Retrievability: Theory and Implementation*, Proceedings of the ACM Workshop on Cloud Computing Security CCSW -09, (2009), 43-54.

44. AF. Barsoum and M.A Hasan, Integrity *Verification of Multiple Data Copies Over Untrusted Cloud Servers*, Proceedings of the 12th IEEE/ACM International Symposium on Cluster, Cloud and Grid Computing, CCGRID-12, (2012),829–34.

45. Y. Zhu, H. Hu, G.J. Ahn, Y. Han and S. Chen, *Collaborative Integrity Verification in Hybrid Clouds*, Proceedings of the 7th International Conference on Collaborative Computing: Networking, Applications, and Work-sharing, COLLABORATECOM-11, (2011), 191-200.

46. A. Mohan and R. Katti, *Provable Data Possession using Sigma-Protocols,* Proceedings of the 11th IEEE International Conference on Trust, Security and Privacy in Computing and Communications, (2012), 565-572.

47. S.R. Tate, R. Vishwanathan and L. Everhart, *Multi-User Dynamic Proofs of Data Possession using Trusted Hardware*, Proceedings of the 3rd ACM Conference on Data and Application Security and Privacy, (2013), 353-364.

48. H. Wang, Proxy Provable Data Possession in Public Clouds, *IEEE Transactions on Services Computing*, **6**(4) (2012), 551-559.

49. H. Shacham and B. Waters, *Compact Proofs of Retrievability*, Proceedings of the International Conference on the Theory and Application of Cryptology and Information Security, TACIS-08, (2008), 90-107.

50. G. Ateniese, R. Burns, R. Curtmola, J. Herring, O. Khan, L. Kissner, Z. Peterson and D. Song, Remote Data Checking Using Provable Data Possession, *ACM Transactions on Information and System Security,* **14**(1) (2011), 1-32.

51. Q. Wang, C. Wang, J. Li, K. Ren and W. Lou, *Enabling Public Verifiability and Data Dynamics for Storage Security in Cloud Computing*, Proceedings of theEuropean Symposium on Research in Computer Security, (2009), 355-370.

52. W. Luo and G. Bai, *Ensuring the Data Integrity in Cloud Data Storage*, Proceedings of the IEEE International Conference on Cloud Computing and Intelligence Systems, CCIS-11, (2011), 240-243.

53. S.T. Shenand W.G. Tzeng, *Delegable Provable Data Possession for Remote Data in the Clouds,* Proceedings of the International Conference on Information and Communications Security, ICS-11, (2011), 93-111.

54. N.Y. Lee and Y.K. Chang, *Hybrid Provable Data Possession at Untrusted Stores in Cloud Computing,*Proceedings of the 17th IEEE International Conference on Parallel and Distributed Systems, IEEEPDS-11, (2011), 638-645.

55. M. Nabeel and E. Bertino, *Privacy Preserving Delegated Access Control in the Storage as A Service Model,* Proceedings of the 13th IEEE International Conference on Information Reuse & Integration, IRI-12, (2012), 645-652.

56. M.A. Alzain and E. Pardede, *Using Multi Shares for Ensuring Privacy in Database-as-a-Service,* Proceedings of the 44th Hawaii International Conference on System Sciences, (2011), 1-9.

57. W.Pugh, Skip Lists: A Probabilistic Alternative to Balanced Trees, *Communications of the ACM,* **33**(6) (1990),668-676.

58. R.C. Merkle, *A Certified Digital Signature*, Proceedings of the ACM Conference on the theory and Application of Cryptology, (1989), 218-238.

59. J. Xu, L. Wei, Y. Zhang, A. Wang, F. Zhou and C.Z. Gao, Dynamic Fully Homomorphic Encryption-Based Merkle Tree for Lightweight Streaming Authenticated Data Structures. *Journal of Network and Computer Applications,* **107** (2018), 113-124.

60. J. Yang, H. Wang, J. Wang, C. Tan and D. Yu. Provable Data Possession of Resource-Constrained Mobile Devices in Cloud Computing, *Journal of Networks,* **6**(7) (2011), 1033-1040.

61. J. Zou, Y. Sun and S. Li, *Dynamic Provable Data Possession Based on Ranked Merkle Hash Tree*, Proceedings of the International Conference on Identification, Information and Knowledge in the Internet of Things, IIKI-16, (2016), 4-9.

62. D. Naor, A. Shenhav and A. Wool, *one-Time Signatures Revisited: Practical Fast Signatures Using Fractal Merkle Tree Traversal*, Proceedings of the 24th IEEE Convention of Electrical & Electronics Engineers in Israel, (2006), 255-259.

63. M.S. Niaz and G. Saake, *Merkle Hash Tree Based Techniques for Data Integrity of Outsourced Data*, Gvd Publishers, (2015), 66-71.

64. S. Peng, Z.Chen and D. Chen, Membership Proof and Verification in Authenticated Skip Lists Based on Heap, *China Communications*, **13**(6) (2016), 195-204.

65. H. Zhao, X. Yaoand X. Zheng, Privacy-Preserving TPA Auditing Scheme Based on Skip List for Cloud Storage, *International Journal of Network Security*, **21**(3)(2019), 451-46.

66. M. Etemad and A. Kupcu, *Transparent,Distributed and Replicated Dynamic Provable Data Possession*, Proceedings of the International Conference on Applied Cryptography and Network Security, ICAN-13, (2013), 1–18.

67. D. Koo, Y. Shin, J. Yun and J. Hur, *An Online Data-Oriented Authentication Based on Merkle Tree with Improved Reliability*, Proceedings of the International Conference on Web Services, ICWS-17, (2017), 840-843.

68. C. Cho, M. Baek and Y. Won, Guaranteeing the Integrity and Reliability of Distributed Personal Information Access Records, *Journal of Ambient Intelligence and Humanized Computing*, (2018),1-8.

69. M. Jakobsson, *Fractal Hash Sequence Representation and Traversal*, Proceedings of the IEEE International Symposium on Information theory, ISIT-02, (2002), 437-444.

70. D. Coppersmith and M. Jakobsson, *Almost Optimal Hash Sequence Traversal*, Proceedings of the International Conference on Financial Cryptography, FC-02, (2002), 102-119.

71. Y. Sella, *On the Computation-Storage Trade-offs of Hash Chain Traversal*, Proceedings ofthe International Conference on Financial Cryptography, FC-03, (2003), 270-285.

72. A. Perrig, R. Canetti, D. Tygar and D. Song, the TESLA Broadcast Authentication Protocol, *Cryptobytes*, **5** (2002), 2-13.

73. Y.-C. Hu, A. Perrig and D.B. Johnson, *Packet Leashes: A Defense Against Wormhole Attacks in Wireless Ad Hoc Networks*, Proceedings of the 22nd Annual Joint Conference of the IEEE Computer and Communications Societies, (2003), 1976-1986.

74. C. Juta and M. Yung, *Pay tree: Amortized-Signature for Flexible Micropayment,* Proceedings of the 2nd USENIX Workshop on Electronic Commerce, (1996),213-221.

75. R. Rivest and A. Shamir, Payword and Micromint–Two Simple Micropayment Schemes, *Cryptobytes*, **2** (1996), 7-11.

76. M. Knecht, W. Meier and C. U. Nicola, *A Space-and Time-Efficient Implementation of the Merkle Tree Traversal Algorithm*, Arxiv Preprint Arxiv:1409.4081, (2014).

77. M. Jakobsson, T. Leighton, S. Micali and M. Szydlo, *Fractal Merkle Tree Representation and Traversal*, Proceedings of the Springer Cryptographers' Track at the RSA Conference, (2003), 314-326.

78. J. Buchmann, E. Damen and M. Schneider, *Merkle Tree Traversal Revisited*, Proceedings of the 2nd International Workshop on Post-Quantum Cryptography, (2008), 63-78.

79. J. Kelsey, *What Should Be in A Parallel Hashing Standard?* [online]Available at https://csrc.nist.gov/events/2014/sha-3-2014-workshop, (2014).

80. K. Atighehchi and A. Bonnecaze, Asymptotic Analysis of Plausible Tree Hash Modes for SHA-3, *IACR Transactions on Symmetric Cryptology,***4** (2017),212-239,https://doi.org/10.13154/tosc.v2017.i4.212-239.

81. D. Berbecaru, *On Creating Digital Evidence in IP Networks with Nettrack*, In Handbook of Research on Network Forensics and Analysis Techniques, (2018), 225-245.

82. J. Mao, Y. Zhang, P. Li, T. Li, Q. Wu and J. Liu, A Position-Aware Merkle Tree for Dynamic Cloud Data Integrity Verification, *Soft Computing*, **21**(8) (2017), 2151-2164.

83. J.Mao, Y. Chen, Y. Zhang, X. Xu, Y. Zhou and J. Liu, Parallel Checking of Content Integrity in Multi- Cloud Storage of Heterogeneous Sensor Systems, *International Journal of Communication Systems*, **30**(5)(2017),https://doi.org/10.1002/dac.3163.

84. H. Tian, Z. Chen, C.C. Chang, M. Kuribayashi, Y. Huang, Y. Cai, Y. Chen and T. Wang, Enabling Public Auditability for Operation Behaviours in Cloud Storage. *Soft Computing*, **21**(8) (2017), 2175-2187.

85. H. Tian, Z. Chen, C.C. Chang, Y. Huang, T. Wang, Z.A. Huang, Y. Cai and Y. Chen, Public Audit for Operation Behaviour Logs with Error Locating in Cloud Storage, *Soft Computing*, **23**(11) (2019), 3779-3792.

86. G. Levitin, L. Xing and Y. Dai, Co-Residence Based Data Vulnerability Vs. Security in Cloud Computing System with Random Server Assignment, *European Journal of Operational Research*, **267**(2) (2018), 676-686.

87. F. Wang, L. Xu, H. Wang and Z. Chen, Identity-Based Non-Repudiable Dynamic Provable Data Possession in Cloud Storage, *Computers& Electrical Engineering*, **69** (2018), 521-533.

88. M.A. Al Zain, E. Pardede, B. Soh and J. A. Thom, *Cloud Computing Security: from Single to Multi-Clouds,* Proceedings of the 45th Hawaii International Conference on System Sciences, (2012), 5490-5499.

89. R. C. Merkle, *A Digital Signature Based on A Conventional Encryption Function*, Proceedings of the Springer Conference on the theory and Application of Cryptographic Techniques, (1987), 369-378.

90. M. Elhoseny, A. Abdelaziz, A. S. Salama, A. M. Riad, K. Muhammad and A. K. Sangaiah, A Hybrid Model of Internet of Things and Cloud Computing to Manage Big Data in Health Services Applications, *Future Generation Computer Systems*, **86** (2018), 1383-1394.

91. J. Bai, A. Song and H. Li, Design and Analysis of Cloud Upper Limb Rehabilitation System Based on Motion Tracking for Post-Stroke Patients, *Applied Science*, **9**(8)(2019), 1620.

92. J. Bai, A. Song, H. Li and B. Xu, Upper Extremity Rehabilitation Training and Assessment System for Home Stroke Patients Based on Workplace Measurement, *China Journal of Science and Instrumentation,* **39**(4)(2018), 74–81.

93. R. L. Rivest, L. Adleman and M. L. Dertouzos, on Data Banks and Privacy Homomorphisms, *Foundations of Secure Computation*, **4**(11) (1978), 169-180.

94. C. Gentry, *Fully Homomorphic Encryption Using Ideal Lattices*, Proceedings of the 41st Annual ACM Symposium on the theory of Computing, STOC-09, (2009) 169-178.

95. C. Gentry, S. Halevi and N. P. Smart, Better *Bootstrapping in Fully Homomorphic Encryption*, Proceedings of the Springer International Workshop on Public Key Cryptography, (2012), 1-16.

96. M. Van Dijk, C. Gentry, S. Halevi and V. Vaikuntanathan, *Fully Homomorphic Encryption Over the Integers*, Proceedings of the Annual International Conference on the theory and Applications of Cryptographic Techniques, (2010), 24-43.

97. R.L. Rivest, A. Shamir and L. Adleman, A Method For Obtaining Digital Signatures and Public-Key Cryptosystems, *Communications of the ACM*, **21** (2) (1978), 120–126.

98. P. Paillier, *Public-Key Cryptosystems Based on Composite Degree Residuosity Classes,* Proceedings of the International Conference on the theory and Applications of Cryptographic Techniques, (1999), 223-238.

99. C.A. Melchor, P. Gaboritand J. Herranz, *Additively Homomorphic Encryption with D-Operand Multiplications*, Proceedings of the Springer Annual Cryptology Conference, (2010), 138-154.

100. J. S. Coron, A. Mandal, D. Naccacheand M. Tibouchi, *Fully HE Over the Integers with Shorter Public Keys*, Proceedings of the Springer Annual Cryptology Conference, (2011), 487-504.

101. J. S. Coron, D. Naccache and M. Tibouchi, *Public Key Compression and Modulus Switching for Fully HE Over the Integers,* Proceedings of the Annual International Conference on the theory and Applications of Cryptographic Techniques, (2012), 446-464.

102. Z. Brakerski, C. Gentry and V. Vaikuntanathan, (Leveled) Fully Homomorphic Encryption without Bootstrapping, *ACM Transactions on Computation Theory,* **6**(3) (2014), 111.

103. C. Gentry, A. Sahai and B. Waters, *Homomorphic Encryption from Learning with Errors:Conceptually-Simpler,Asymptotically-Faster,Attribute-Based,* Proceedings of the Springer Annual Cryptology Conference, (2013), 75-92.

104. J. Fan and F. Vercauteren, *Somewhat Practical Fully Homomorphic Encryption,* IACR Cryptology Eprint Archive, **144** (2012).

105. Z. Brakerski, *Fully Homomorphic Encryption without Modulus Switching from Classical Gapsvp*, Proceedings of the Annual Cryptology Conference, (2012), 868-886.

106. A. Atayero and O. Feyisetan, Security Issues in Cloud Computing: The Potentials of Homomorphic Encryption, *Journal of Emerging Trends in Computing and Information Sciences*, **2**(10) (2011), 546-552.

107. G. Asharov, A. Jain, A. López-Alt, E. Tromer, V. Vaikuntanathan and D. Wichs, *Multiparty Computation with Low Communication, Computation and Interaction Via Threshold FHE*, Proceedings of the Springer Annual International Conference on the theory and Applications of Cryptographic Techniques, (2012), 483-501.

108. M. Naehrig, K. Lauter and V. Vaikuntanathan, *Can Homomorphic Encryption Be Practical,* Proceedings of the3rd ACM Workshop on Cloud Computing Security Workshop, (2011),113-124.

109. H. Hu, J. Xu, C. Ren, and B. Choi, *Processing Private Queries Over Untrusted Data Cloud Through Privacy Homomorphism*, Proceedings of the 27th IEEE International Conference Data Engineering, (2011), 601-612.

110. Q. B. Hani and J. P. Dichter, *Data Leakage Prevention Using Homomorphic Encryption in Cloud Computing*, Proceedings of the IEEE Systems, Applications and Technology Conference, (2016), 1-5.

111. J. Kubiatowicz, D. Bindel, Y. Chen, P. Eaton, D. Geels, R. Gummadi, S. Rhea, H. Weatherspoon, W. Weimer, C. Wells and B. Zhao, *Oceanstore: An Architecture for Global-Scale Persistent Storage*, Proceedings of the 9th International Conference on Architectural Support for Programming Languages and Operating Systems, ASPLOS-IX, (2000), 190-201.

112. J. Hur and D. K. Noh, Attribute-Based Access Control with Efficient Revocation in Data Outsourcing Systems, *IEEE Transactions on Parallel and Distributed Systems*, **22**(7) (2010), 1214-1221.

113. Q. Wang, C. Wang, K. Ren, W. Lou and J. Li, Enabling Public Auditability and Data Dynamics for Storage Security in Cloud Computing, *IEEE Transactions on Parallel and Distributed Systems*, **22**(5) (2010), 847-59.

114. E. Stefanov, M. V. Djjk, A. Oprea and A. Juels, *Iris: A Scalable Cloud File System with Efficient Integrity Checks*, Proceedings of the Annual Computer Security Applications Conference, (2012), 229-238.

115. L. Xue, J. Ni, Y. Li and J. Shen, Provable Data Transfer from Provable Data Possession and Deletion in Cloud Storage, *Computer Standards and Interfaces*, **54**(2017), 46-54.

116. J. He, Y. Wu, Y. Dong, Y. Zhang and W. Zhou, Dynamic Multidimensional Index for Large-Scale Cloud Data, *Journal of Cloud Computing*, **5**(1) (2016),10- 15.

117. S. Micali, *Efficient Certificate Revocation*, U.S. Patent No. 7,337,315, (2008).

118. P. Berman, M. Karpinski and Y. Nekrich, Optimal Trade-off for Merkle Tree Traversal, *Theoretical Computer Science*, **372**(1)(2007), 26-36.

119. M. Sicuranza, A. Esposito and M. Ciampi, An Access Control Model to Minimize the Data Exchange in the Information Retrieval, *Journal of Ambient Intelligence and Humanized Computing*, **6**(6) (2015), 741–752.

120. V. López-Jaquero, F. Montero and M. A. Teruel, Influence Awareness: Considering Motivation in Computer-Assisted Rehabilitation, *Journal of Ambient Intelligence and Humanized Computing,***10**(6) (2019), 2185–2197.

121. R. Gennaro R, C. Gentry and B. Parno, *Non-Interactive Verifiable Computing: Outsourcing Computation to Untrusted Workers*, Proceedings of the Springer International Symposium Advances in Cryptology, CRYPTO-10, Lecture Notes in Computer Science, **6223**, (2010), 465–482.

122. F. Eltayesh, J. Bentahar, R. Mizouni, H. Otrok and E. Shakshuki, Refined Game-theoretic Approach to Improve Authenticity of Outsourced Databases, *Journal of Ambient Intelligence and Humanized Computing*, **8**(3) (2017), 329–344.

123. C. Wan, J. Zhang, B. Pei and C. Chen, Efficient Privacy-Preserving Third-Party Auditing for Ambient Intelligence Systems, *Journal of Ambient Intelligence and Humanized Computing,* **7**(1) (2016), 21-27.

124. M.S. Kiraz, A Comprehensive Meta-Analysis of Cryptographic Security Mechanisms for Cloud Computing, *Journal of Ambient Intelligence and Humanized Computing*, **7**(5) (2016), 731–760.

125. F. Li, D. Xie, W. Gao, K. Chen, G. Wang and R. Metere, A Certificateless Signature Scheme and A Certificateless Public Auditing Scheme with Authority Trust Level 3, Journal *of Ambient Intelligence and Humanized Computing*, (2017) 1-10.

126. S. Hohenberger and A. Lysyanskaya, *How to Securely Outsource Cryptographic Computations,* Proceedings of the Springer theory of Cryptography Conference, (2005), 264-282.

127. C. Xiang and C. Tang, Efficient Outsourcing Schemes of Modular Exponentiations with Checkability For Untrusted Cloud Server, *Journal of Ambient Intelligence and Humanized Computing*, **6**(1) (2015), 131–139.

128. P.K. Premkamal, S.K. Pasupuleti and P.J.A. Alphonse, A New Verifiable Outsourced Ciphertext-Policy Attribute-Based Encryption for Big Data Privacy and Access Control in Cloud, *Journal of Ambient Intelligence and Humanized Computing*, **10**(7) (2019), 2693–2707.

129. T. Wang, B. Yang, H. Liu, Y. Yu, G. Qiu and Z. Xia, An Alternative Approach to Public Cloud Data Auditing Supporting Data Dynamics, *Soft Computing*, **23**(13) (2019), 4939-4953.

130. A. Khedr, G. Gulak and V. Vaikuntanathan, SHIELD: Scalable Homomorphic Implementation of Encrypted Data-Classifiers, *IEEE Transactions on Computers*, **65**(9)(2015), 2848-2858.

131. I. Chillotti, N. Gama, M. Georgieva and M. Izabachene, *Faster Fully Homomorphic Encryption: Bootstrapping in Less Than 0.1 Seconds,* Proceedings of the International Conference on the theory and Application of Cryptology and Information Security, ASIACRYPT-16, (2016), 3-33.

132. J. Alperin-Sheriff and C. Peikert, *Faster Bootstrapping with Polynomial Error*, Proceedings of the Springer Annual Cryptology Conference, (2014)297- 314.

133. J. F. Biasse and L. Ruiz, *FHEW with Efficient Multibit Bootstrapping*, Proceedings of the Springer International Conference on Cryptology and Information Security in Latin America, (2015), 119-135.

134. L. Ducas and D. Micciancio, *FHEW: Bootstrapping Homomorphic Encryption in Less Than A Second*, Proceedings of the Springer Annual International Conference on the theory and Applications of Cryptographic Techniques, (2015), 617-640.

135. G. Bonnoron, *A Journey towards Practical Fully Homomorphic Encryption,* (Doctoral Dissertation) (2018).

136. R. Gennaro, C. Gentry and B. Parno, *Non-Interactive Verifiable Computing: Outsourcing Computation to Untrusted Workers*, Proceedings of the Springer Annual Cryptology Conference, (2010), 465-482.

137. Elaine Barker and Allen Roginsky, *Transitioning the Use of Cryptographic Algorithms and Key Lengths*, NIST Special Publication 800-131A Revision 1 & 2, (2015) (2019), https://doi.org/10.6028/NIST.SP.800-131Ar2.

Milton Keynes UK
Ingram Content Group UK Ltd.
UKHW032329131223
434291UK00013B/705